PEARSON LONGMAN
KEYSTONE
E

PEARSON English Learning System

Workbook

Anna Uhl Chamot

John De Mado

Sharroky Hollie

PEARSON

Upper Saddle River, New Jersey • Boston, Massachusetts • Chandler, Arizona • Glenview, Illinois

PEARSON LONGMAN
KEYSTONE E

PEARSON English Learning System

Workbook

Staff credits: The people who made up the *Longman Keystone* team, representing editorial, production, design, manufacturing, and marketing, are John Ade, Rhea Banker, Liz Barker, Danielle Belfiore, Virginia Bernard, Kenna Bourke, Anne Boynton-Trigg, Jeffrey Buckner, Johnnie Farmer, Patrice Fraccio, Charles Green, Henry Hild, David L. Jones, Lucille M. Kennedy, Ed Lamprich, Emily Lippincott, Tara Maceyak, Maria Pia Marrella, Linda Moser, Laurie Neaman, Sherri Pemberton, Liza Pleva, Joan Poole, Edie Pullman, Tania Saiz-Sousa, Chris Siley, Lynn Sobotta, Jennifer Stem, Jane Townsend, Marian Wassner, Lauren Weidenman, and Adina Zoltan.

Smithsonian American Art Museum contributors: Project director and writer: Elizabeth K. Eder, Ph.D.; Writer: Mary Collins; Image research assistants: Laurel Fehrenbach, Katherine G. Stilwill, and Sally Otis; Rights and reproductions: Richard H. Sorensen and Leslie G. Green; Building photograph by Tim Hursley.

Cover Image: Background, John Foxx/Getty Images; Inset, Jon Berkeley/Getty Images
Text composition: TSI Graphics

Text font: 11 pt ITC Stone Sans Std
Photos: 11, Lan O'Leary/Dorling Kindersley; 14, Shutterstock; 28, Bonnie Kamin/PhotoEdit; 47, Dana White/PhotoEdit; 54, Dana White/PhotoEdit; 61, Shutterstock; 87, Gunter Marx/ Dorling Kindersley Media; 94, Holiday House; 108, Larry Downing/Reuters/CORBIS; 127, Walter Hodges/Taxi/Getty Images; 131, Photo of the author courtesy of Johnny Ball Productions; 134, Shutterstock; 141, Haywood Magee/Hulton-Deutsch Collection/CORBIS; 148, Marvin Koner/Stock Photo/Black Star; 167, Fulvio Roiter/CORBIS; 174, Shutterstock; 181, Charles Gullung/Zefa/CORBIS; 188, H. Schmid/Zefa/CORBIS; 207, Archivo Iconografico, S.A./Bettmann/CORBIS; 214, China Photos/Getty Images; 221, Shutterstock; 228, Bettmann/CORBIS.
Illustrations: Rick Powell 7; Leah Palmer Preiss 21; Tomo Narashima 25; Ron Mazzellan 101; Tom Leonard 131
Technical art: TSI Graphics

ISBN-13: 978-1-4284-3509-4
ISBN-10: 1-4284-3509-3

Printed in the United States of America
15   18

Contents

Unit 1

Unit 2

Unit 3

Contents

Unit 4

Unit 5

READING 1

READING 2

READING 3

READING 4

READING 5

Unit 6

READING 1

READING 2

READING 3

READING 4

READING 5

TEST PREPARATION

Contents

Name _____ Date _____

Why should we reach out to others?

READING 1: From *Criss-Cross* / "Oranges"

VOCABULARY **Literary Words** *Use with textbook page 5.*

> **REMEMBER** Writers use **characterization** to help the reader know what the characters are like. The **setting** is the actual place and time the story happens. **Figurative language** is writing that the reader isn't supposed to take literally, such as a metaphor. It can help you relate to the cultural and historical setting.

Read the sentences. Write whether the sentences describe characterization, tell the setting of the story, or show figurative language.

characterization	Jamal always helped elderly people to cross the street.
1.	The old house had a cozy feel and smelled of cinnamon.
2.	His heart was a hard, lifeless rock.
3.	Alice gave Sally a look of pure envy.
4.	The kitten was a little cottonball, soft and white.
5.	The American prairie was like an ocean of grass; it stretched as far as the eye could see.

Read the passage. Circle clues that tell about the setting. Underline parts of the passage that contain examples of characterization. Put a star next to phrases that use figurative language.

> The sandy beach had been lit by a golden light all summer. Now that it was late fall, the beach seemed so different. The ocean was a large, restless creature. It shimmered dark blue. The sky was gray and the sand was beige. Except for Rob, there wasn't a single person on the beach. Rob began making a fire on the beach and asked all his friends to come today to spend one more day with him here. Tomorrow, he would leave to fight a war in a distant country. All he wanted was just one carefree day when he could enjoy the company of his good friends.

Read the paragraph below. Pay attention to the underlined academic words.

Last summer, my sisters and I decided to repaint my grandmother's house. The paint was old, and water was causing some <u>external</u> damage to the wood. It was a big <u>project</u>. Before we began, we had to choose the paint color. We had to <u>visualize</u> what each color would look like. We finally chose brown. As we painted, we had to <u>interact</u> with each other often. Working on this project gave me a new <u>perspective</u> on the importance of teamwork.

Match each word with its definition.

Example: ___d___ interact

a. form a picture of someone or something in your mind

_____ **1.** external

b. on the outside

_____ **2.** visualize

c. a carefully planned piece of work

_____ **3.** project

d. talk to other people and work together with them

_____ **4.** perspective

e. a way of thinking about something

Use the academic words from the exercise above to complete the sentences.

5. When you work with a team, you need to be able to _____ with others.

6. Great runners always _____ a race before they run it.

7. When Sean looked at the problem from his brother's _____, he changed his mind.

8. Ahmad painted a picture of his sister for his art _____.

Complete the sentences with your own ideas.

Example: From the beautiful external details of the castle, I can guess that the inside is
_____*also very grand*_____.

9. When I want to relax, I like to visualize _____.

10. When I interact with someone new, I often _____.

Name _____ Date _____

REMEMBER Double /s and rs can occur in the middle and at the end of a word.

Read the words in the box. Then write each word in the correct column.

tomorrow   excellent   doll   fulfill   parrot   occurrence   hill   quarrel   burr   intelligence

Double *l*		Double *r*	
Middle of Word	**End of Word**	**Middle of Word**	**End of Word**

Choose five words from the box above. Write a sentence for each of the words.

1. _____

2. _____

3. _____

4. _____

5. _____

> **REMEMBER** As you read, visualize by using the details to make a picture in your mind. When you visualize what you read, you use your imagination to help you understand the text.

Read the paragraphs. Underline the details that help you visualize the character, object, or scene.

1. The sound of pens scratching against paper filled the room. Jesse anxiously looked at his test paper. Sweat ran down his pale face. He felt his heart beating.

2. The diary was dusty. The pages had turned yellow. The edges of the pages were soft from having been used often. The cover was faded blue. The cover had the words "My Secrets" in small, rounded letters.

3. Mr. Hanson sat on his usual park bench. His newspaper was scattered around him. Today, his bald freckled head was covered with a woolen cap. He wore a heavy red jacket and black pants. The skin around his eyes wrinkled as he smiled at people passing by.

Read the paragraphs. Draw sketches of the way you visualize the scene.

4. I heard a noise on my porch. When I opened the door, I saw an old, tired dog with long dirty fur. His large sad eyes looked at me as if to ask "Would you please take me home?"

5. The mountain and all the earth surrounding it shook. A huge burst of black smoke shot up from the top of the mountain. Ash filled the sky. Rocks crashed down the sides of the mountain along with orange streams of lava.

COMPREHENSION   *Use with textbook page 17.*

Choose the best answer for each item. Circle the letter of the correct answer.

1. In the excerpt from *Criss-Cross,* Debbie's mother thought that Debbie was _____.

    a. lazy   **b.** heroic   **c.** shy

2. Mrs. Bruning told Debbie that it was going to rain because she _____.

    a. needed help closing   **b.** needed Debbie to find   **c.** needed help with
        the windows   an umbrella for her   her laundry

3. Mrs. Bruning's kitchen was _____.

    a. full of unfinished projects   **b.** messy with dishes   **c.** very neat and tidy
                                    everywhere

4. A detail that helps you visualize the outside of Mrs. Bruning's house is _____.

    a. "ivy climbing up the stone"   **b.** "a bottle of vinegar...   **c.** "her steps were small,
                                  with legs"   baby steps"

5. In "Oranges," the lady in the drugstore knew the boy didn't have _____.

    a. enough oranges   **b.** warm clothes   **c.** enough money

RESPONSE TO LITERATURE   *Use with textbook page 17.*

Which words or phrases in the poem "Oranges" best helped you visualize the setting? Write them below.

_____

_____

_____

In your own words, describe the weather in "Oranges."

_____

_____

_____

Compound and Complex Sentences *Use with textbook page 18.*

> **REMEMBER** Compound sentences are made of two independent clauses. They show contrast with the conjunctions *yet* or *but*. Complex sentences are made up of an independent clause and a dependent clause. They show contrast with *even though*, *although*, or *though* in the dependent clause.

Read the following sentences. Write whether they are compound or complex sentences.

Example: _____*complex*_____ Although I like castles, I've never been to one.

1. _____ Ancient castles were huge, but later castles were gigantic.

2. _____ Although many ancient castles are now in ruins, some are still standing.

3. _____ Most castles are in Europe, though some are in Asia.

4. _____ Castles look beautiful, but they are often cold inside.

5. _____ Some people live in castles, even though they are expensive.

Follow the directions to combine the pairs of sentences and form compound or complex sentences.

6. (Write a complex sentence with "although.") That house is brand-new. The design is traditional.

_____

7. (Write a compound sentence with "yet.") Today log houses can be very pleasant. Originally they were uncomfortable.

_____

8. (Write a compound sentence with "but.") It looks modern. That house is old.

_____

9. (Write a complex sentence with "even though.") It is fifty years old. Our house is energy efficient.

_____

10. (Write a complex sentence with "though.") Our house is large. The rooms are small.

_____

Unit 1 • Reading 1

WRITING

Describe a Place *Use with textbook page 19.*

This is the word web that Andrew completed before writing his paragraph.

Mrs. Bruning's House

old and run-down

like a castle

ivy on the wall

Complete your own word webs about Mrs. Bruning's house from the perspective of her son. Include sensory details. Complete one word web for the inside of the house and another for the outside of the house.

outside

inside

Why should we reach out to others?

READING 2: "Managing Stress"

VOCABULARY **Key Words** *Use with textbook page 21.*

Write each word in the box next to its definition.

maximize	moderation	stressful	stressors	systematic	threshold

Example: ___*maximize*___: to increase or make as big as possible

1. _____: carefully organized and thoroughly done

2. _____: makes one worry a lot

3. _____: avoiding extremes; not being too much or too little

4. _____: the level at which something causes an effect

5. _____: things that cause anxiety

Use the words in the box at the top of the page to complete the sentences.

6. Some airlines put as many seats as possible in their airplanes to

   _____ the number of passengers.

7. Moving to a new house can be very _____ for children and
   adults alike.

8. Max has a very low _____ for pain, and he was very uncomfortable
   when his new sneakers gave him blisters.

9. My textbook presents information in an organized, _____ way.

10. Fried, salty foods are not healthful, so eat them in _____.

VOCABULARY   **Academic Words** *Use with textbook page 22.*

Read the paragraph below. Pay attention to the underlined academic words.

> There are many <u>factors</u> that influence health. Exercise, eating, and sleeping habits can influence health. A stressful <u>environment</u> can also affect health. In addition, some <u>individuals</u> are naturally healthier than others. For example, each person <u>responds</u> differently to illness. Because we are all <u>unique</u>, disease affects us in different ways. An illness that might last a day or two for one person might last much longer for another person.

Write the academic words from the paragraph above next to their correct definitions.

Example: _____*factors*_____: one of several things that cause or influence a situation

1. _____: different from all others

2. _____: one person separate from others

3. _____: the situations, things, and people that affect the way in which people live

4. _____: react or answer

Use the academic words from the exercise above to complete the sentences.

5. These green and orange flowers are very _____.

6. My father's new job was one of the _____ that led us to move.

7. She likes living in the city because she enjoys a busy, exciting _____.

Complete the sentences with your own ideas.

Example: Some people respond to scary movies by _*screaming or grabbing*_
*someone's hand*.

8. Something that makes me unique is _____.

9. The most interesting individual I know is _____.

10. I live in an environment that is _____.

> **REMEMBER** Words that come from the same base word often have related meanings. Knowing the meaning of a base word plus the meaning of common prefixes and suffixes can help you figure out word meanings. **Example:** The words *tolerate* and *tolerable* have related meanings. *Tolerate* means "to accept something, even though you do not like it." *Tolerable* means "able to be tolerated, or not very good, but acceptable."

Read each pair of related words below. Circle any prefixes or suffixes that help you figure out the meaning of the words. Then look up each word in a dictionary and write a definition for it in your own words.

1. **a.** tolerance _____

   b. intolerance _____

2. **a.** excitable _____

   b. excitement _____

3. **a.** research _____

   b. researchers _____

4. **a.** tears _____

   b. tearfulness _____

5. **a.** system _____

   b. systematic _____

Choose a word from each pair of related words above. Write a sentence for each of the words.

6. _____

7. _____

8. _____

9. _____

10. _____

READING STRATEGY | PREVIEW | *Use with textbook page 23.*

REMEMBER Before you read an article, preview it by asking yourself "What is this article about?" When you preview, think about what you already know about the topic. Then look at the title, headings, pictures, photographs, charts, graphs, and maps.

Preview the following article. Then answer the questions.

Healthy Eating

How healthy are you? The U.S. Department of Agriculture (USDA) has put together guidelines for staying healthy. These guidelines say to eat a balanced diet and to get a lot of exercise.

Healthful Foods

Variety is the key to a balanced diet. For the average adult, the USDA recommends eating the following each day:
• 6 ounces of grains, such as cereal or pasta
• 2 ½ cups of vegetables
• 2 cups of fruit (not juice)
• 3 cups of milk, yogurt, or other dairy products
• 5 ½ ounces of meat, chicken, fish, beans, or nuts

Limiting Fats and Sugar

Most of the fat you eat should come from vegetables, nuts, and fish. Do not eat too much solid fat. Margarine and shortening contain trans fat. This kind of fat will cause health problems. Also limit the amount of sugar you eat. Sugar contains no nutrients.

1. Circle the first thing you looked at when you previewed the article.

2. What else did you pay attention to? Write an *X* next to each part that helped you to preview.

3. What do you think the article will be about?

   _____

4. What parts of the article helped you to answer question 3?

   _____

5. What do you want to know about the topic? Set a purpose for reading the article.

   _____

Choose the best answer for each item. Circle the letter of the correct answer.

1. People react to stressful events _____.

    a. in different ways   **b.** the same way   **c.** by avoiding change

2. To some degree, any change is _____.

    a. enjoyable   **b.** stressful   **c.** healthy

3. A healthy diet includes plenty of _____.

    a. protein-rich foods   **b.** fat and sugar   **c.** fruits and vegetables

4. Exercise and a healthy diet help you _____.

    a. manage stress better   **b.** become more nervous   **c.** overreact to problems

5. Sharing problems with a friend can _____.

    a. make your problems seem worse   **b.** help you feel loved and valued   **c.** increase signs of osteoporosis

EXTENSION *Use with textbook page 31.*

Imagine you have a friend in a stressful situation. Based on what you learned in the article, what advice would you give him or her? Fill in the chart with five things you would tell your friend to do to manage his or her stress.

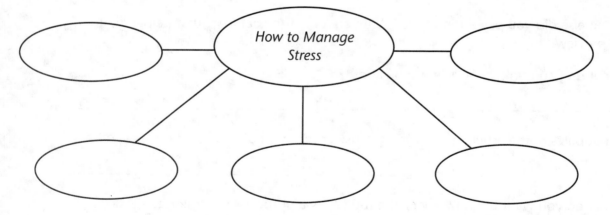

GRAMMAR

Can/Can't + Verb for Ability or Possibility *Use with textbook page 32.*

> **REMEMBER** *Can* is a modal auxiliary (or helping verb). It is followed by a verb in its base form. You can use *can* to tell what someone is good at (ability). You can also use *can* to describe what a person can do to overcome his or her shortcomings (possibility). The negative of *can* is *can't*.

Read the following sentences. Write whether *can* shows ability or possibility.

Example: ___*possibility*___ If he is unhappy, he can talk to a friend or
family member.

1. _____ My sister can play the piano beautifully.

2. _____ If he wants to lose weight, he can eat a healthier diet and get
more exercise.

3. _____ Carlos is always calm and can manage stress very well.

4. _____ A healthcare professional can give advice on many issues.

5. _____ You can try some relaxation techniques to help you relax.

Complete the sentences with *can* or *can't* + the verb in parentheses.

Example: (problem solve) My brother is smart and ___*can problem solve*___
very well.

6. (improve) Eating a nutritious diet _____ your health.

7. (relax) She's always tense, so she _____ easily.

8. (incorporate) Anyone _____ exercise into his or
her life.

9. (understand) If you _____ the problem, you can't find
a solution.

10. (be) Even imagining change _____ stressful for
some people.

Describe a Person *Use with textbook page 33.*

This is the word web that Michael completed before writing his paragraph.

Complete your own word web about a stressed-out person. List what the person can or can't do, as well as the person's physical and character traits.

Name _____ Date _____

Why should we reach out to others?

READING 3: From *The Phantom Tollbooth* / "Grandma Ling"

VOCABULARY   **Literary Words** *Use with textbook page 35.*

REMEMBER An **allegory** is a type of story that can be understood in two ways. The story has a literal meaning and one or more symbolic meanings. **Irony** is what an author uses when words suggest something very different from their usual meanings. A **narrative poem** tells a story, much like a novel does.

Read the sentences. Write whether the sentences describe *allegory, irony,* **or are from a** *narrative poem.*

narrative poem	I walked down the road by day, Coming toward me was Mrs. Clay.
1.	While walking and playing his video game, Jason fell into the Hole of Wasted Time.
2.	It was a dark and stormy night. Mr. Embers came calling.
3.	I had the best birthday ever – no one at school remembered.
4.	"That was so funny I forgot to laugh," she said.

Read this allegorical fable by Aesop. Then answer the questions.

On a hot summer day, Fox was walking in a garden, and he passed a tree with a bunch of grapes on a high branch. Fox was very hungry and wanted those grapes. "Those look like the sweetest grapes in the world," said Fox. He ran and jumped, but he didn't reach the grapes. He tried again and again, but the grapes were still out of his reach. Finally, he walked away and said, "I'm sure those grapes taste sour."

5. In this fable, the grapes have a symbolic meaning. What do they represent?

_____

_____

Read the paragraph below. Pay attention to the underlined academic words.

> The <u>concept</u> of a time machine is fascinating. For example, with a time machine one might be able to land <u>precisely</u> at a certain time and place. One might <u>schedule</u> a trip to ancient Egypt to <u>analyze</u> the culture there. Up to now, though, no one has invented a time machine and time travel has yet to <u>occur</u>. In fact, most scientists <u>conclude</u> that time travel is impossible.

Match each word with its definition.

Example: ___*b*___ occur   **a.** plan; list of times and events

_____ **1.** analyze   **b.** happen; take place

_____ **2.** concept   **c.** reach a decision based on facts or logic

_____ **3.** conclude   **d.** examine something in detail in order to understand it

_____ **4.** precisely   **e.** an idea or thought

_____ **5.** schedule   **f.** exactly

Use the academic words from the exercise above to complete the sentences.

6. After reading the research, I _____ that your ideas are correct.

7. Max wanted to paint the walls of his room _____ the same shade of yellow as the carpet.

8. The scientist wrote a computer program to help her _____ the results of her experiment.

Complete the sentences with your own ideas.

Example: The train schedule tells me ___*what time the train leaves for New York*___.

9. The concept of freedom and equality for all is _____.

10. _____ could not occur in real life.

WORD STUDY **Synonyms** *Use with textbook page 37.*

REMEMBER Synonyms are two or more words that have the same or similar meanings.
Example: *to fear / to be afraid*
Synonyms are used to make your writing more interesting, or to express different shades of meaning.
Example: He *heard* me, but he didn't *listen*.

Read the words in the box. Then write each word in the column next to its synonym.

easy	help	shout	design	strange	angry

Word	Synonym
aid	*help*
1. yell	
2. simple	
3. mad	
4. plan	
5. odd	

Complete the sentences with a synonym for the word in parentheses.

Example: (small) She had a _____*little*_____ flower in her hand.

6. (huge) They were digging a(n) _____ hole next to our house.

7. (contest) The best team will win the _____.

8. (stress) I cannot _____ enough how important it is to study every day.

9. (purchase) Where did you _____ this beautiful sweater?

10. (ill) He was too _____ to come to school today.

Use with textbook page 37.

REMEMBER A problem is a difficult situation that a character in a story faces. The solution is the way the problem is fixed. Identifying problems and solutions in a story will help you better understand it.

Write whether the sentences tell about a problem or about a solution in a story.

problem	Rosa stood on stage in silence. She had forgotten the words to the song.
1.	Manny didn't want to tell his friends that he was afraid of dogs.
2.	After much arguing, the team decided to go with Joyce's plan.
3.	"Oh no!" shouted the chef. "My oven just broke!"
4.	Glenn realized that he and Jon were friends after all.
5.	Sal wanted to learn how to swim—but he didn't have money for lessons.

Read the paragraphs. Underline the problems and circle the solutions.

6. Sam worried about her new school. She had just moved to town, and she would be the only new kid in the ninth grade. "I just need to be myself," she thought, "and be friendly."

7. Sam went into a classroom. The teacher asked, "Who are you?"
   "Isn't this the ninth-grade English class?" asked Sam.
   "No, this is the tenth-grade English class," said the teacher kindly. "Go to Room 307."
   Sam picked up her backpack and went to Room 307.

8. Sam grabbed the doorknob to Room 307. It came off right in her hand! Sam knocked loudly on the door. The teacher opened it and said, "You must be our new student!"
   "Yes, I am," smiled Sam.

Answer the following questions.

9. What are some of the problems that Sam faces?

_____

10. How are Sam's problems solved?

_____

COMPREHENSION   *Use with textbook page 44.*

Choose the best answer for each item. Circle the letter of the correct answer.

1. The Lethargarians spend most of their day _____.

   a. doing nothing   **b.** eating cookies   **c.** thinking seriously

2. The watchdog looks like _____.

   a. a bear   **b.** a clock   **c.** a lion

3. Milo's main problem is that he _____.

   a. doesn't know how to   **b.** is afraid of the   **c.** does not know how
       leave the Doldrums   watchdog   to build a tollbooth

4. The Doldrums is an allegory for where you go if you are _____.

   a. learning how to drive   **b.** interested in traveling   **c.** not using your mind

5. In this story, Milo learns _____.

   a. the importance of   **b.** the value of a   **c.** how to travel in space
       daydreaming   little thought   and time

RESPONSE to LITERATURE   *Use with textbook page 45.*

Of the two readings, *The Phantom Tollbooth* and "Grandma Ling," which is more meaningful to you? Why?

_____

_____

_____

_____

_____

_____

_____

Simple Present for Habitual Actions or Routines *Use with textbook page 46.*

REMEMBER Use the simple present to talk about routines or things that happen regularly. Use words like *always, never, every day*, and *twice a day* to tell how often they occur. *Always* and *never* go before a regular verb. *Every day* or *twice a day* usually come after the verb or later in the sentence.

Rewrite the sentences so that they describe routines or things that happen regularly to you or someone else. Use expressions like *always, never, every day*, or *twice a day*.

Example: I read the sports section in the newspaper.

I read the sports section in the newspaper every day.

1. I take an afternoon or early evening nap.

_____

2. My English teacher gives me a lot of homework.

_____

3. I stay home all day and loaf around.

_____

4. My best friend calls me on the phone.

_____

5. I stay up very late at night studying for tests.

_____

Write five sentences that describe routines or things that happen regularly to you or someone else. Use expressions like *always, never, every day*, or *twice a day*.

Example: *My mother always asks me to help wash the dishes.*

6. _____

7. _____

8. _____

9. _____

10. _____

Name _____ Date _____

WRITING

Describe an Event *Use with textbook page 47.*

This is the sequence chart that Chas completed before writing his paragraph.

First
Milo notices some strange creatures.

↓

Next
He finds out that everybody does nothing except for the watchdog.

↓

Then
The watchdog comes and Milo talks to it.

↓

Finally
The watchdog tells Milo how to escape the Doldrums.

Complete your own sequence chart about an event. Describe the event in chronological order. Use your sequence chart when you write your paragraph.

First

↓

Next

↓

Then

↓

Finally

Why should we reach out to others?

READING 4: "Your Brain and Nervous System"

VOCABULARY **Key Words** *Use with textbook page 49.*

Write each word in the box next to its definition.

behavior	nerves	neurons	organ	relays	system

Example: ___*neurons*___ : nerve cells

1. _____ : pathways that bring information from the brain to the body and from the body back to the brain

2. _____ : a group of parts that work together

3. _____ : a part of a living thing that has a set purpose or function

4. _____ : sends a message or information from one person, thing, or place to another person, thing, or place

5. _____ : things that a person does or says

Use the words in the box at the top of the page to complete the sentences.

6. Your brain contains billions of cells called _____.

7. The heart is an _____ that pumps blood throughout the body.

8. The students were rewarded for their excellent _____ during class.

9. The mouth and stomach are parts of the body's _____ that digests food.

10. If you bump your head, your body _____ that information to your brain.

VOCABULARY   Academic Words *Use with textbook page 50.*

Read the paragraph. Pay attention to the underlined academic words.

> Our brain, of course, allows us to think. Thinking may seem like a simple <u>process</u>, but it's actually very complex. For example, the left side of the brain is <u>analytical</u>. It uses reason to draw <u>logical</u> conclusions. The <u>function</u> of the right side of the brain is to control creative thought. These two parts of the brain allow us to be more <u>adaptable</u>; they help us respond differently to different situations. Besides allowing us to think, our brain also gives instructions to the rest of the body. For example, it sends messages that tell the body how to <u>react</u> to heat or cold.

Write academic words from the paragraph next to their correct definitions.

Example: ____*process*____: a series of actions

1. _____: change in response to a message or stimulus

2. _____: able to use reason

3. _____: able to use logic

4. _____: purpose; action that a thing performs

5. _____: able to adjust

Use the academic words from the paragraph to complete the sentences.

6. The writing _____ involves drafting, revising, and editing.

7. Many plants are _____ and can survive in many different types of soil.

8. Shivering is one way your body will _____ to cold weather.

Complete the sentences with your own ideas.

Example: The function of the brake on a car is to make the car
____*stop or slow down*____.

9. All five children in the Milano family play soccer. Julia is the youngest and has just started playing. A logical conclusion is that Julia _____.

10. An analytical thinker can figure out _____.

REMEMBER Etymology is the study of the origin and history of words. Many English words come from Greek or Latin word parts, called roots. Knowing the meanings of these roots can often help you figure out the meanings of many words, especially scientific terms.

Study the chart below. Notice the relationships between the roots, their meanings, and the English words that contain them.

Root	Meaning	Origin	English Words
gen/genos	birth, source, producing	Greek	gene, genesis
thermos	warm, hot	Greek	thermometer, thermal
hypnos	sleep, dream	Greek	hypnosis, hypnotic
dens/dentis	tooth	Latin	dentist, dental
lingua	tongue	Latin	linguistics, multilingual

Choose the words from the box below that best complete each sentence. The first answer is done for you.

dream-like	generation	languages	temperature	false teeth	~~produces~~

Example: A **generator** is a machine that _____*produces*_____ energy.

1. A **geneticist** is someone who studies the passing on of traits from one

   _____ to another.

2. You can use a **thermostat** to keep a room at a specific _____.

3. Some people are easier to **hypnotize** than others; they quickly fall into a

   _____ state.

4. Sometimes people have to wear **dentures**, or _____, to replace the natural ones they have lost.

5. People who are **bilingual** speak two _____, or tongues.

Name _____ Date _____

REMEMBER When you read a science article, look at all the pictures, charts, or diagrams. These visuals will help you to understand the ideas in the article.

Look at the diagram and follow the directions.

Physical Structure of the Brain

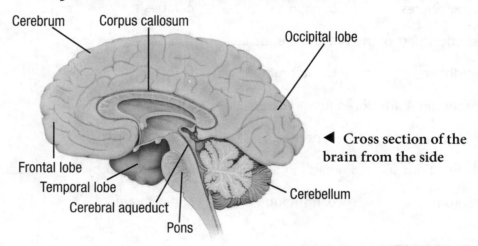

Cerebrum   Corpus callosum   Occipital lobe

◀ **Cross section of the brain from the side**

Frontal lobe
Temporal lobe
Cerebral aqueduct
Pons
Cerebellum

1. Read and underline the title of the diagram.

2. Read and circle the labels that tell you what each part of the diagram shows.

3. Imagine this visual is included in an article you are going to read. What do you think the article will be about?

   _____

   _____

4. Imagine that a sentence in the article tells you about "where memories are stored in the brain." How do you think this visual could help you learn where memories are stored?

   _____

   _____

5. Would a science article without visuals teach you just as well about a topic as an article with visuals? Explain your reasoning.

   _____

   _____

   _____

Choose the best answer for each item. Circle the letter of the correct answer.

1. The brain sends messages to your body through the _____.

   a. spinal cord   **b.** stomach   **c.** heart

2. Tiny cells in the nervous system are called _____.

   a. hemispheres   **b.** neurons   **c.** lobes

3. The largest part of the brain is the _____.

   a. hindbrain   **b.** midbrain   **c.** forebrain

4. Our memories are stored in our _____.

   a. brains   **b.** nerves   **c.** spinal cords

5. Body functions such as breathing and blinking are controlled by the _____.

   a. neurons   **b.** right lobe   **c.** hindbrain

EXTENSION *Use with textbook page 57.*

Think about the different functions of the left and right sides of the brain. In the chart below, write some activities you do using each side of your brain.

Left Side: Logical, Analytical	Right Side: Creative, Intuitive, Subjective
figuring out how much change you'll get at the store	*painting a picture*

GRAMMAR

Complex and Compound-Complex Sentences *Use with textbook page 58.*

> **REMEMBER** A complex sentence has one independent clause and one or more dependent clauses. A compound-complex sentence has two or more independent clauses and one or more dependent clauses. Dependent clauses often begin with *because, since, although, even though, when, while,* or *as.* The words *but, and, yet, or,* and *so* often join independent clauses.

Read the sentences. Underline independent clauses in each sentence and circle any dependent clauses. Then write *C* on the line if the sentences are complex. Write *CC* on the line if they are compound-complex sentences.

___*C*___ **Example:** (While the left side of the brain is logical,) the right side is intuitive.

_____ **1.** Because your brain needs new challenges all the time, you should avoid following the same routine every day.

_____ **2.** When you are solving puzzles, you are thinking, and thinking is exercise for the brain.

_____ **3.** Take good care of your brain because it cannot be repaired easily, and you cannot buy replacement parts for it.

Follow the directions in parentheses to join each group of clauses. Join independent clauses with *but, and, yet, or,* or *so.* Begin dependent clauses with *although, as, because, even though, since, though, while,* or *when.*

Example: (Write a compound-complex sentence.) People are tired. They yawn. Scientists are not sure why.

  When people are tired, they yawn, but scientists are not sure why.

4. (Write a compound-complex sentence.) Scientists are interested in sleep. They have studied it carefully. They still have much to learn.

  _____

5. (Write a complex sentence.) Most animals sleep regularly. Some animals sleep a lot more than others.

  _____

Describe an Object *Use with textbook page 59.*

This is the graphic organizer that Ashley completed before writing her paragraph.

> **Front**
> *forebrain controls memory, intelligence, and speech*

↓

> **Middle**
> *midbrain controls messages going in and out of brain*

↓

> **Back**
> *hindbrain controls balance, movement, and coordination*

Complete your own graphic organizer about another part of the body or any object that can be described using spatial organization.

>

↓

>

↓

>

UNIT 1

Why should we reach out to others?

READING 5: "Sally Mason" and "Cowboy Blues"

VOCABULARY **Etymology and Connotation** *Use with textbook page 61.*

REMEMBER **Etymology** explains where a word comes from, what it meant long ago, or how it once sounded. For example, *barnacle* comes from the Middle English *barnakille,* first recorded in the fifteenth century, meaning "shellfish." Also, sometimes words with the same definition have different **connotations**, or emotional meanings.

Use a dictionary to find the origin of each word listed in the chart. List its first recorded date of use and its original meaning.

Word	Origin	Date
Example: vacation	*From the Latin "vacare," meaning freedom, exemption*	*1300s*
raccoon		
abandon		
habit		
grin		

Match the words in column A to the correct etymologies in column B. Use a dictionary if you need help.

Column A   **Column B**
1. punch   Latin *innocentem,* meaning "not guilty"
2. innocent   Sanskrit *panchan,* meaning "mixed drink"
3. collapse   Old French *lavandarium,* meaning "things to be washed"
4. laundry   Latin *collapsus,* meaning "fall together"

Use a dictionary to write the connotations of the words below.

5. grin, smirk _____ _____

> **REMEMBER** **Figurative language** requires the reader to use his or her imagination to grasp the full meaning of a written idea or image. Figurative language includes metaphors, similes, and personification.

Read the following sentences. Identify the type of figurative language being used as an example of metaphor, simile, or personification. Then explain the statement's meaning.

1. The sky fell asleep. _____

_____

2. The stars twinkled in the sky like diamonds. _____

_____

3. Mr. Robinson is as stubborn as a brick wall. _____

_____

4. She kept her secrets safely tucked away in her pockets. _____

_____

5. The sweat on my forehead was as slippery as ice. _____

_____

6. Mom's laugh ran wild through the room. _____

_____

7. Her teeth came out of hiding when she heard his hilarious joke. _____

_____

8. The children played with the idea of giving their teacher a surprise party. _____

_____

9. The girls were lined along the wall like five cans of vegetables. _____

_____

10. The sun was a golden blanket across the sky. _____

_____

LITERARY ANALYSIS Relating Figurative Language to Time and Culture *Use with textbook page 63.*

REMEMBER **Figurative language** is often shaped by the **time** and **culture** in which it is written. A poet's choice to use a particular metaphor or symbol is frequently inspired by the time and culture in which he or she writes.

Read the excerpt from Walt Whitman's "When Lilacs Last in the Dooryard Bloom'd." Consider the fact that this poem was written after the assassination of President Abraham Lincoln in the spring of 1865. Then answer the questions below.

When lilacs last in the door-yard bloom'd,
And the great star early droop'd in the western sky in the night,
I mourn'd—and yet shall mourn with ever-returning spring.

O ever-returning spring! trinity sure to me you bring;
Lilac blooming perennial, and drooping star in the west,
And thought of him I love.

O powerful, western, fallen star!
O shades of night! O moody, tearful night!
O great star disappear'd! O the black murk that hides the star!
O cruel hands that hold me powerless! O helpless soul of me!
O harsh surrounding cloud, that will not free my soul!

1. Why do you think Whitman decided to use the image of blooming lilacs and "ever-returning spring"?

_____

_____

2. What do you think the following line means: "the great star early droop'd in the western sky in the night, / I mourn'd"?

_____

_____

REMEMBER Meter, rhyme scheme, and stanzas are different poetic devices that poets use to express their ideas and create poems.

Identify each poetic device defined below. Write *meter, rhyme scheme,* or *stanza* on the line.

1. A unit within a poem, similar to a paragraph, is called a _____.

2. The recurring rhythmical pattern of stressed and unstressed syllables is

   called _____.

3. The way a poem's rhymes are arranged is called _____.

Using your knowledge of rhyme scheme, write four lines of poetry that reflect the patterns listed below.

4. *aabb*

   _____

   _____

   _____

   _____

5. *abab*

   _____

   _____

   _____

   _____

Write two lines of poetry. Make the syllables alternate between stressed and unstressed sounds.

6. _____

   _____

LITERARY ANALYSIS **Poetic Forms** *Use with textbook page 65.*

Read Shakespeare's Sonnet 30 below. The poem is about friendship. Identify and label the four stanzas and the couplet. Then determine the rhyme scheme used and write the appropriate letter (*a, b, c, d,* etc.) at the end of each line. Finally, mark each syllable in the first four lines as "stressed" or "unstressed." Mark a stressed syllable with an "X" and an unstressed syllable with a "/"

When to the sessions of sweet silent thought   _____

I summon up remembrance of things past,   _____

I sigh the lack of many a thing I sought,   _____

And with old woes new wail my dear time's waste;   _____

Then can I drown an eye, unused to flow,   _____

For precious friends hid in death's dateless night,   _____

And weep afresh love's long-since-cancell'd woe,   _____

And moan the expense of many a vanish'd sight.   _____

Then can I grieve at grievances foregone   _____

And heavily from woe to woe tell o'er   _____

The sad account of fore-bemoaned moan,   _____

Which I new pay as if not paid before: _____

But if the while I think on thee, dear friend,   _____

all losses are restored, and sorrows end.   _____

Possessive Case *Use with textbook pages 70–71.*

REMEMBER Possessive nouns are used to show possession or ownership. They are words that normally function as nouns—people, places, or things—but take on a special role when used to describe other nouns. Remember also that possessive nouns generally end with an *'s*. Some possessive pronouns modify nouns. Others stand alone and do not modify nouns.

Each of the following sentences requires a possessive noun. Underline the singular or plural noun that should be possessive and rewrite it with the appropriate ending.

1. Coach Hammond practices are always challenging. _____

2. Marianne enthusiasm is contagious. _____

3. Reading is the childrens favorite subject. _____

4. My new book cover is already torn. _____

5. Mr. Taylor assignments are very helpful. _____

6. My three dogs leashes are missing. _____

7. The principal parking space was taken. _____

8. The brothers voices sound very similar. _____

Read the following sentences. Underline the possessive pronouns in the first sentence, and then circle the correct possessive pronoun in the second sentence.

1. He won a scholarship. It's hers / his / mine.

2. Could you please return my shirt? It's mine / your / theirs.

3. We have a duty to clean up the park. It's theirs / ours / mine.

WRITING **Write a Poem** *Use with textbook pages 72–73.*

Before you plan the content and structure of your poem, spend some time choosing the topic of your poem. You will need to think not only about the topic, but also about the message you want to send.

Remember, a poem can be about any topic. Choose something that is important and meaningful to you.

Here are some general topics to help you brainstorm: friendship, family, relationships, community, growing older, work, memories, questions about life, challenges you've had.

Answer the following questions to get started.

What is a topic that interests you?	
Why is it important to you?	
What message do you want to send to the reader?	
What examples, experiences, or feelings do you have about this topic?	
How can you make this topic interesting to the reader?	

WRITING

> **REMEMBER** A poem should combine all of the necessary poetic elements (language, structure, meaning) with your own personal vision. What you say in your poem and how you say it is up to you—the poet. A little planning will help you make the best of your imagination.

List your ideas for the content, structure, and language of your poem below. The different sections will help guide you.

Topic/Theme of Poem	Poetic Form (sonnet, ballad, haiku, or free verse?)
Civic duty is very important. I would like to inspire more people to get involved in their communities.	*Sonnet* **Rhyme Scheme** *ababcdcdefefgg*

Examples/Details
One person can make a difference; Doing nothing harms others.

Ways to Use Figurative Language (symbol, metaphor, simile, personification)
Symbol of an outstretched hand = willingness to help others

Complete your own chart below.

Topic/Theme of Poem	Poetic Form
_____ _____ _____	_____ **Rhyme Scheme** _____

Examples/Details
_____
_____
_____

Ways to Use Figurative Language (symbol, metaphor, simile, personification)
_____
_____
_____

Unit 1

EDIT AND PROOFREAD   *Use with textbook page 82.*

Read the paragraph carefully. Look for mistakes in spelling, punctuation, and grammar. Correct the mistakes with the editing marks on Student Book page 563. Then rewrite the paragraph correctly on the lines below.

> Taking an exam be can a stressful process but it must be done. The furst thing you should do on the mornin of an exam is wake up on time. Be shure to set an alarm clok so that you don't oversleep. When wake up, take a shower and get dressed. Then have a good breakfast. Its very important to eat before a test That way youll have a lot of energy to work hard on the exam. Come to the exam prepared with any pencels or pens that you mite need. Take several Deep breaths at the beginning of the exam this will relax you and help you to focus.

_____

_____

_____

_____

_____

_____

_____

_____

_____

_____

Underline the vocabulary items you know and can use well. Review and practice any you haven't underlined. Underline them when you know them well.

Literary Words	Key Words		Academic Words	
characterization	maximize	behavior	external	concept
setting	moderation	nerves	interact	conclude
figurative language	stressful	neurons	perspective	occur
allegory	stressors	organ	project	precisely
narrative poem	systematic	relays	visualize	schedule
irony	threshold	system	environment	adaptable
			factors	analytical
			individual	function
			respond	logical
			unique	process
			analyze	react

Put a check by the skills you can perform well. Review and practice any you haven't checked off. Check them off when you can perform them well.

Skills	I can . . .
Word Study	☐ recognize and spell words with double *l*s and *r*s. ☐ recognize and use related words. ☐ recognize and use synonyms. ☐ recognize the roots of words. ☐ recognize and use etymology and connotation.
Reading Strategies	☐ visualize. ☐ identify problems and solutions. ☐ preview. ☐ use visuals.
Grammar	☐ use compound and complex sentences. ☐ use *can* or *can't* + verb for ability or possibility. ☐ use simple present for habitual actions or routines. ☐ use complex and compound-complex sentences. ☐ use possessive case correctly.
Writing	☐ describe a place. ☐ describe a person. ☐ describe an event. ☐ describe an object. ☐ write a poem. ☐ write a descriptive essay.

Visual Literacy: Smithsonian American Art Museum *Use with textbook pages 84–85.*

LEARNING TO LOOK

All artists use the same elements of art, such as line, shape, space, texture, and color to compose an artwork. Look at *Dowager in a Wheelchair* by Philip Evergood on page 84 in your textbook. In the box below, draw the straight lines that you see in the painting (the lines that the artist used to compose this street scene).

Example:

INTERPRETATION

Look at *Dowager in a Wheelchair* again. Pretend you are walking down the street in the painting. Then answer the questions.

What do you **SEE**?

Example: *I see a lot of buildings.* _____

_____

What do you **HEAR**?

_____

What do you **FEEL**?

_____

Unit 1 • Visual Literacy: Smithsonian American Art Museum

5W&H

Look at *Reach Out #3* by Yuriko Yamaguchi on page 85 in your textbook. If you could interview Yuriko Yamaguchi about this work of art, what would you ask her? Use *Who, Where, When, What, Why,* and *How* to shape your questions.

Example: Why *did you make this sculpture?* _____

1. Who _____

   _____

2. Where _____

   _____

3. When _____

   _____

4. What _____

   _____

5. Why _____

   _____

6. How _____

   _____

Name _____ Date _____

What shapes our identity?

READING 1: From *Finding Miracles* / "A Conversation with Julia Alvarez"

VOCABULARY **Literary Words** *Use with textbook page 89.*

> **REMEMBER** A **conflict** is a struggle or problem in a story. A conflict can either be internal (inside) the character, or external (outside) the character. A dilemma, where a character faces two different choices of action, is one type of internal conflict. A story is usually told from a character's **point of view**. A story told in the first-person point of view is told through the eyes of the main character. A story told in the third-person point of view is told by a narrator who is not the main character of the story.

Read the sentences. Write whether the conflict is external or internal.

internal	I have always wanted to learn to fly a plane, but I am afraid of heights.
1.	I want to go ice skating, but it is raining so they closed the rink.
2.	I want to finish my homework, but I just can't force myself to concentrate.
3.	I was going to play at my friend's house, but my parents won't let me.

Read this passage from the fable "The Ants and the Grasshopper." Underline an example of conflict. Then answer the questions that follow.

The Ants and the Grasshopper

It was summer, and the ants were working hard. Grasshopper was not working. He was lying around, enjoying the sun. The ants said to Grasshopper, "You should not be relaxing. You should be working hard. You should be storing food for the winter." Grasshopper got angry and said, "Don't tell me what to do. If I want to relax all summer, that is exactly what I am going to do."

---

4. What point of view is the story told in? _____

5. Explain the conflict between Grasshopper and the ants.

_____

Read the paragraph below. Pay attention to the underlined academic words.

> It was difficult for Sarah to <u>adapt</u> to her new school. She didn't want to <u>reveal</u> that her father was a famous writer. In the past it had been an <u>issue</u> because some people had liked her just because her father was famous. She wanted to avoid this <u>conflict</u> at her new school. She wanted to be liked because of her own personality. She didn't want her <u>identity</u> to be defined by her father. She didn't want to have to <u>interpret</u> the behavior of her new friends.

Write the academic words from the paragraph above next to their correct definitions.

Example: _____*reveal*_____: make something known that was previously secret

1. _____: adjust to a new environment

2. _____: a situation of having to choose between opposing things

3. _____: who someone is

4. _____: clarify the meaning of something

5. _____: a subject or problem that people discuss

Use the academic words from the exercise above to complete the sentences.

6. Some plants _____ to the cold and adjust by dropping their leaves.

7. Sam's _____ with his parents was about which college he should attend.

8. Luis did not _____ the secret.

Complete the sentences with your own ideas.

Example: My parents want to discuss the issue with ___*our neighbors*_____.

9. Our identity is important to us because _____.

10. Could you please interpret _____?

WORD STUDY   Diphthongs /ou/ and /oi/ *Use with textbook page 91.*

REMEMBER Some words have a special sound called a diphthong. The diphthong /ou/ can be spelled *ow* as in *clown* and *ou* as in *mouse*. The diphthong /oi/ can be spelled *oi* as in *loin* and *oy* as in *coy*. Learning the patterns can help you say and spell many words correctly.

Read the words in the box below. Then write each word in the correct column in the chart.

crown	rejoin	town	sirloin	noun
disappoint	profound	decoy	drown	employ

/ou/ spelled *ow, ou*	/oi/ spelled *oi, oy*
crown	

Write the sound-spelling pattern in each word below.

Example: soy _____/oi/ spelled oy_____

1. frown _____

2. spoil _____

3. around _____

4. annoy _____

5. gown _____

6. boil _____

Use with textbook page 91.

REMEMBER A cause is a reason that something happens. What happens as the result of the cause is the effect. The words *so, since, therefore, as a result of,* and *because* often link a cause and its effect. **Example:** Because of the storm, many houses were damaged. In the example, the cause is the storm and the effect is that many houses were damaged.

Read the following sentences. Underline the causes. Circle the effects.

Example: (People cannot live in the middle of the desert), because it is too hot.

1. Because she lost her passport, she couldn't leave the country.

2. Last night was cloudy, so we could not see any stars in the sky.

3. I like stars and planets, so I read more about them in a book.

Read the paragraphs. Then answer the questions that follow.

4. Rita was late for class. Since she was rushing, she got on the first bus she saw. Then she realized she was on the wrong bus.

   What is the cause? _____

   What is the effect? _____

5. Albert was hungry. When he found a hot dog stand, he bought two hot dogs.

   What is the cause? _____

   What is the effect? _____

COMPREHENSION *Use with textbook page 98.*

Choose the best answer for each item. Circle the letter of the correct answer.

1. Milly says that she always has a big problem with _____.

   a. writing   **b.** math   **c.** science

2. Mrs. Kaufman tells her students that we put our lives together with _____.

   a. friendships   **b.** stories   **c.** travel

3. When Milly gets upset, her hands get _____.

   a. very cold   **b.** stiff and blue   **c.** red and itchy

4. Milly writes about _____.

   a. The Box   **b.** Em, her best friend   **c.** the cold Vermont weather

5. Milly and Pablo are alike because they both are _____.

   a. in jeans and a sweater   **b.** trying to graduate early   **c.** from the same country

RESPONSE TO LITERATURE *Use with textbook page 99.*

Find a paragraph that you like very much in the story. Draw a picture illustrating it.

Modals for Ability, Possibility, or Necessity *Use with textbook page 100.*

> **REMEMBER** The modal auxiliaries *can* and *could* are often used to express present and past ability. *Could, may,* and *might* are often used to express possibility. *Have to* and *must* express necessity.

Complete the sentences with phrases from the box.

must be	had to sing	could solve	might go	can speak

1. In 5th grade, Marcia _____ any math problem in her workbook.

2. Last night, I _____ on stage in the school play.

3. Today, Juan _____ English fluently.

4. You _____ on time for school.

5. It is such a beautiful day that we _____ for a swim.

Complete the sentences with *can, could, has to, have to,* or *had to* and the verb in parentheses.

6. (hear) During the storm yesterday, he _____ waves crashing against the rocks.

7. (see) When it is not cloudy, we _____ the mountains from our house.

8. (shovel) After the winter storm, we _____ snow for hours.

9. (comfort) Every time it thunders, they _____ the dog.

10. (play) You _____ a game with your friends instead of watching television.

WRITING

Explain the Steps in a Process *Use with textbook page 101.*

This is the sequence chart that Karimah completed before writing her paragraph.

> **First**
> *Meet with a guidance counselor or teacher.*

↓

> **Next**
> *Try to relax and be confident.*

↓

> **Last**
> *Ask other students questions about the school.*

Complete your own sequence chart explaining the steps in a process. Describe the steps in chronological order.

> **First**

↓

> **Next**

↓

> **Last**

What shapes our identity?

READING 2: From *What Do You Stand For? For Teens: A Guide to Building Character*

VOCABULARY   **Key Words** *Use with textbook page 103.*

Write each word from the box next to its definition below.

character traits	empathy	influences	inventory	relationships	tolerant

Example: ___*empathy*___: the ability to understand someone else's feelings

1. _____: accepting of others

2. _____: a survey or checklist

3. _____: aspects of personality

4. _____: the way two people or groups behave toward each other

5. _____: powers that have an effect on the way someone thinks or develops

:e the words from the box at the top of the page to complete the sentences.

Maria's parents are major _____ on her actions.

People who are _____ respect and accept other people's opinions.

.uis has two major _____: he is kind and hard-working.

/hen Alexis feels bad, her parents show their _____ by hugging her.

me _____ last a lifetime, while other connections with people last hort time.

Name _____ Date _____

VOCABULARY **Academic Words** *Use with textbook page 104.*

Read the paragraph below. Pay attention to the underlined academic words.

> Next time you react to someone who makes you angry, think about what <u>category</u> your <u>response</u> would fit in. Is it a helpful, mature response or a childish, manipulative response? Instead of acting childishly, act like an <u>adult</u>. Remember that <u>communication</u> is important. Don't try to control the other person by <u>manipulating</u> him or her. Instead, express your feelings honestly and listen carefully to the other person. Maintain a positive <u>attitude</u>, and try to work out an understanding.

Match each word with its definition.

Example: ___*f*___ response

_____ 1. categories

_____ 2. manipulating

_____ 3. adult

_____ 4. attitude

_____ 5. communication

a. opinions and feelings

b. making someone do what you want by deceiving or influencing him or her

c. process of speaking, writing, etc.

d. groups or divisions of things

e. a grown-up person

f. something said, written, or done as a reaction to something else

Use the academic words from the exercise above to complete the sentences.

6. No one likes Rick because he is always _____ his friends by lying to them.

7. Lisa has a cheerful _____, even when things go badly.

8. Give a quick _____ when someone invites you to a party.

Complete the sentences with your own ideas.

Example: An adult I admire a lot is __*my mother, because she is smart and kind*__.

9. My favorite form of communication is _____.

10. My favorite books fall into these categories: _____.

Use with textbook page 105.

> **REMEMBER** Collocations are words that are used together. The verbs *make* and *take* sometimes form collocations with other words.

Complete the sentences with collocations from the box.

take on	take apart	take after	make an appointment	make believe	make do

Example: I ___take after___ my father. We both love to play soccer.

1. My younger sister likes to _____ that she's a princess.

2. If your tooth hurts, you'd better _____ to see the dentist.

3. I'll have to _____ this watch to put in a new battery.

4. My grandparents don't have a lot of money, but they _____.

5. He is very adventurous and likes to _____ new challenges.

Write five more collocations with *make* or *take* in the chart below. Use a dictionary if needed. Then write a sentence for each.

Collocation with *make* or *take*	Sentence
make up	We argued yesterday, but today we made up.
6.	
7.	
8.	
9.	
10.	

READING STRATEGY **CLASSIFY** *Use with textbook page 105.*

> **REMEMBER** When you read, you often classify things by putting them into groups. The groups may be about characters, interests, relationships, or any other category.

Read the following paragraphs. Circle the things you would classify as belonging to a group. Then write the name of the group on the line.

Example: The cook worked in a big restaurant in the city. She used many kinds of spices in the foods she prepared. The spices she used were (garlic,) (saffron,) and (basil).
Circle the words. What group do these items belong to? _____ *spices*

1. Chris has a gardening business in the neighborhood. He mows lawns and cuts hedges. He also waters the flowers and bushes.

   Circle the words. What group do these items belong to?

   _____

2. Lisa liked all kinds of sports. She was on the school softball team. She played soccer with her friends. Her favorite game was basketball.

   Circle the words. What group do these items belong to?

   _____

3. When Tom went to the school carnival, he played several games. First, he took part in ring-toss. Then, he went to the guess-the-number booth. Finally, he joined his friends in the potato-sack race.

   Circle the words. What group do these items belong to?

   _____

4. June had a party. Her sister Alice, Aunt Martha, and Uncle Tom came. Her parents were there, too.

   Circle the words. What group do these items belong to?

   _____

5. Everyone in Mrs. Callebro's class had to read books and write reports. Glenda read *A Step from Heaven*. Jason finished *Finding Miracles*. Bill read *Crime Scene Detectives*.

   Circle the words. What group do these items belong to?

   _____

COMPREHENSION   *Use with textbook page 110.*

Choose the best answer for each item. Circle the letter of the correct answer.

1. People who like to talk about "what if" situations _____.

    a. like practical solutions   **b.** like taking risks   **c.** like schedules

2. People who prefer to know how things work enjoy _____.

    a. real, concrete   **b.** columns and figures   **c.** lectures and abstract ideas
    experiences

3. Character traits include all of the following BUT _____.

    a. being a leader   **b.** building cupboards   **c.** having self-discipline

4. Interest inventories help you figure out _____.

    a. what you like to do   **b.** how you learn   **c.** how you get along
    with others

5. A relationship inventory includes all the following BUT _____.

    a. talking with kids   **b.** liking your teachers   **c.** telling a story

EXTENSION   *Use with textbook page 111.*

Write facts about yourself in each category on the chart below.

Learning Styles	Character Traits	Interests	Relationships

Write a brief description of yourself based on your learning styles, character traits, interests, and relationships.

_____

_____

_____

_____

_____

GRAMMAR

Preference with *would* + *rather* + Verb and Unreal Conditional

Use with textbook page 112.

> **REMEMBER** To ask about or express a preference, use *would rather*. **Example:** I would rather be spending time with my friends than doing my chores. Use the unreal conditional to describe what you're not doing now but would like to do. Unreal conditional sentences have an *if* clause and a result clause. Use the simple past form of the verb in the *if* clause. (If the verb is *be*, use *were*.) Use *would* or *might* + the base form of the verb in the result clause.

Complete the sentences with phrases or clauses from the box.

If I could go anywhere	He would rather travel	she would sleep late
You would rather	I would rather live	

1. _____, I would go to California.

2. _____ anywhere than stay home.

3. If she were on vacation, _____.

4. _____ watch gymnastics than soccer.

5. _____ in the city than in the suburbs.

Complete the sentences with the appropriate form of the verb or verbs in parentheses. Use *would rather* to ask about or state a preference. Use *would* or *might* to express the unreal conditional. Use each verb in the correct tense or form. Remember: if the verb in the "if clause" is *be*, use *were*.

6. (be, play) If I _____ taller, I

   _____ on the basketball team.

7. (have, watch) If my little brother _____ more courage,

   he _____ scary movies.

8. (see, read) _____ you _____

   a movie or _____ a book?

9. (chew) My dog _____ on my shoes than on his bone.

10. (be, catch) If our cat _____ faster, he

    _____ more mice.

WRITING

Explain How Something Is Classified *Use with textbook page 113.*

This is the word web that Chelsea completed before writing her paragraph.

Character
Traits
Inventory

traits I would
like to have or
strengthen

trait to
work on
first

Complete your own word web about the Learning Styles Inventory, **Relationships Inventory,** or **Interests Inventory.** Show how the inventory can be interpreted using classification.

Name _____ Date _____

UNIT 2

What shapes our identity?

READING 3: "An Interview with An Na" /
From *A Step from Heaven* / "Learning English"

VOCABULARY **Literary Words** *Use with textbook page 115.*

REMEMBER The **theme** is the central message or insight into life that you get from reading a work of literature. **Suspense** is a feeling of uncertainty about the outcome of events in a piece of literature.

Read the following paragraphs. Then answer the questions that follow.

> Carla had spent months training for the race. She knew she could win it. When the race started, she ran ahead of all the other runners. She could hear the other runners behind her. She could feel them catching up to her. Up ahead she saw the finish line. She could taste victory.

1. What words create a feeling of suspense? _____

2. What is the theme of the paragraph? _____

> Tim planned for the bike trip. He packed everything he thought he needed in a backpack. As he biked up a hill, he heard thunder and saw lightning. He felt raindrops. When the storm struck, Tim kept dry inside his tent.

3. What words create a feeling of suspense? _____

4. What is the theme of the paragraph? _____

Write a brief paragraph on a theme of your choice. Make sure that your paragraph contains suspense.

_____

_____

_____

_____

Read the paragraph below. Pay attention to the underlined academic words.

> The young Korean woman hoped to <u>achieve</u> success as a professional artist. She loved to <u>construct</u> images of people and animals out of clay. Her parents did not think this work would provide her with an <u>adequate</u> amount of money. They put <u>emphasis</u> on the importance of a high-paying job. In her <u>culture</u>, she was taught to respect the wishes of her parents. She wanted to respect them, but she had to follow her dream. Their <u>perception</u> of her career choice changed when her artwork began to sell.

Write the academic words from the paragraph above next to their correct definitions.

Example: ___*perception*___: seeing or noticing; ability to perceive

1. _____: make by placing parts together

2. _____: special importance

3. _____: succeed in getting a good result

4. _____: enough; satisfactory but not excellent

5. _____: type of civilization; art, food, social norms of a civilization

Use the academic words from the exercise above to complete the sentences.

Example: Visiting Tokyo was a great way to learn about Japanese ___*culture*___.

6. Because he worked very hard, Mayor Smith was able to _____ a great deal.

7. Luke plans to _____ a birdhouse from wood.

8. The family puts _____ on holidays because they are important to them.

Complete the sentences with your own ideas.

Example: My friend is very interested in the culture of

*China since she was born there*.

9. My perception is that _____.

10. An adequate breakfast includes _____.

Name _____ Date _____

WORD STUDY **Spelling Long _a_** *Use with textbook page 117.*

REMEMBER The long _a_ sound can be spelled several different ways. These include _a_e_ as in _grade_, _ay_ as in _play_, and _ai_ as in _raise_. Knowing these patterns will help you spell words with the long _a_ sound correctly.

Read the words in the box below. Then write each word in the correct column in the chart.

| ~~brake~~ | grain | bay | plain | snail | clay |
| gray | brave | chase | stray | whale | faint |

Long _a_ spelled _a_e_	Long _a_ spelled _ay_	Long _a_ spelled _ai_
brake		

Complete the incomplete words with _a_e, ay,_ or _ai_ to spell the long _a_ sound.

1. We took the tr_____n into the city.

2. The singer ran onto the st_____g_____.

3. Madrid is the capital of Sp_____n.

4. He's heavy and has a large w_____st.

5. What are you going to do tod_____?

6. I like apple and gr_____p_____ juice.

7. The students compl_____ned about the test.

8. My sister was drawing with cr_____ons.

9. We asked the w_____tress for the bill.

Unit 2 • Reading 3   **57**

Use with textbook page 117.

> **REMEMBER** An author's purpose is the author's reason for writing something. An author's purpose can be to inform, to entertain, or to persuade. To find out the author's purpose, ask yourself, "Why did the author write it?"

Read each passage. Identify whether the author's purpose is to entertain, inform, or persuade.

1. You should buy Smiley Toothpaste because it will make your teeth white and shiny. It is the best toothpaste you can buy. Four out of five dentists say so. Buy it today!

   What is the author's purpose for writing this passage? _____

   _____

2. The riddle in the book was "If I have 10 oranges in one hand and 12 oranges in the other hand, what do I have?" The answer is "Big hands!"

   What is the author's purpose for writing this passage? _____

   _____

3. China is a nation in East Asia. It has one of the world's richest cultures. For example, paper, the compass, and printing were all invented in China. Chinese literature dates back as far as the year 1000 B.C.E.

   What is the author's purpose for writing this passage? _____

   _____

4. You should recycle all your cans and bottles because it helps reduce litter. It will make our town cleaner. Plus, it is better for the environment. So be sure to recycle today.

   What is the author's purpose for writing this passage? _____

   _____

5. The pyramids are the oldest stone structures in the world. The Egyptians built them about 5,000 years ago. They are also among the tallest structures in the world. The largest pyramid is taller than a 40-story building.

   What is the author's purpose for writing this passage? _____

   _____

COMPREHENSION   *Use with textbook page 124.*

Choose the best answer for each item. Circle the letter of the correct answer.

1. Young Ju Park tells the class that _____.

   a. her family is moving   **b.** she likes spaghetti   **c.** her brother died

2. The class makes Young Ju Park _____.

   a. scratch-and-sniff stickers   **b.** yarn toys called warm fuzzies   **c.** drawings with glue and glitter

3. The school sends the family _____.

   a. fresh fish   **b.** books   **c.** flowers

4. Young Ju Park tells her babysitter Gomo that she _____.

   a. lost the spelling contest   **b.** has no friends   **c.** wants to improve her English

5. At the end of the story, Young Ju Park is glad that her mother _____.

   a. works hard during the day   **b.** is her teacher at school   **c.** did not discover her lie

RESPONSE to LITERATURE   *Use with textbook page 125.*

Explain what parts of life in America are most difficult for Young Ju Park. Write a paragraph in which you discuss at least two different aspects of her new life. Use details from the story in your paragraph.

_____

_____

_____

_____

_____

_____

_____

Have to + Verb for Necessity and
Supposed to be + Verb (*-ing*) for Expectation *Use with textbook page 126.*

> **REMEMBER** To express a necessity to do something, use *have to* + the base form of a verb.
> **Example:** I *have to do* my homework. To express something you are expected to do but are either not
> doing or not obligated to do, use *supposed to be* + the *-ing* form of a verb or *supposed to* + the base
> form of a verb. **Example:** I am *supposed to be* in math class right now.

Complete the sentences with phrases from the box.

supposed to obey	has to make	supposed to be studying	has to watch	have to pass

1. I am _____ for a science test.

2. When her mother is away, she _____ her little sister.

3. Because his father is away, the boy _____ dinner.

4. To get a driver's license, you _____ a test.

5. Drivers are _____ the rules of the road.

**Complete the sentences with *has to, have to, supposed to,* or *supposed to be* and the
verb in parentheses. Use the verbs in the correct form.**

6. (be) We are _____ quiet when the baby is sleeping.

7. (visit) He _____ his grandparents this weekend.

8. (make) My mother is _____ a cake for my
grandmother's birthday.

9. (read) You are _____ the directions before you begin
making cookies.

10. (experiment) To be a good cook, you _____ in the kitchen.

WRITING

Write a Cause-and-Effect Paragraph *Use with textbook page 127.*

This is the cause-and-effect chart that Will completed before writing his paragraph.

Cause
lying for attention

↓

Effects
*more lying to cover up first lie, greater risk of being
caught, feeling very scared and guilty.*

Complete your own cause-and-effect chart about someone who did something
wrong and the effects of his or her actions.

Cause

↓

Effects

What shapes our identity?

READING 4: From *Crime Scene: How Investigators Use Science to Track Down the Bad Guys*

VOCABULARY   **Key Words** *Use with textbook page 129.*

Write each word from the box next to its definition below.

authorized	biometric	captivity	data bank	genetic	laser	technologies

Example: ___*biometric*___ : the measurement of physical characteristics such as fingerprints to prove someone's identity

1. _____: information on a subject stored in a computer system

2. _____: relating to a tiny unit that makes up a section on a chromosome

3. _____: a tool that sends out a very narrow and strong beam of light

4. _____: using scientific or industrial methods

5. _____: given official permission

6. _____: the state of being kept as a prisoner or in a very small space

Use the words from the box at the top of the page to complete the sentences.

7. The printing press and plow are examples of old _____, while computers and cell phones are examples of new ones.

8. At a zoo, you can see many animals in _____.

9. The police officer used a _____ device to prove the prisoner's identity.

10. Police put pictures of fingerprints into a _____ so they can access them quickly on the computer.

VOCABULARY   **Academic Words** *Use with textbook page 130.*

Read the paragraph below. Pay attention to the underlined academic words.

> Fingerprints are a very <u>distinctive</u> physical trait. No two people have <u>identical</u> fingerprints. Fingerprints are sometimes used in forms of <u>identification</u>, such as passports. They are also sometimes used as <u>evidence</u> in criminal cases. When a lawbreaker touches something with his or her bare hands, fingerprints are left on the surface. The prints might be <u>invisible</u> to the eye, but police can treat them with powder or chemicals to make them <u>visible</u>.

Match each word with its definition.

Example: ___*c*___ identical

_____ 1. visible

_____ 2. identification

_____ 3. distinctive

_____ 4. invisible

_____ 5. evidence

a. clearly marking a person or thing as different from others

b. facts, objects, or signs that show something exists or is true

c. exactly the same

d. official documents that prove who you are

e. not able to be seen

f. clear; able to be seen

Use the academic words from the exercise above to complete the sentences.

6. The police collected many clues to use as _____ against the criminal.

7. The criminal had a _____ scar that was very unusual.

8. The two photographs are _____, so they look exactly the same.

Complete the sentences with your own ideas.

Example: For identification, my mother uses her __*driver's license*_____.

9. If I were an invisible superhero, I would _____.

10. On a clear night, here is what is visible in the sky:

_____.

REMEMBER Compound words are two words joined together to make a new one. Compound words can be either two separate words, as in *reading glasses*, two words spelled as one, as in *notebook*, or two words connected with a hyphen, as in *follow-up*.

Complete the sentences with compound words formed from the words in the box.

high	stick	absent	gum	~~soft~~	chewing	week	school
hand	~~boiled~~	bag	end	ground	play	minded	lip

Example: I like _____*soft-boiled*_____ eggs best.

1. _____ that contains sugar is bad for your teeth.

2. Is your new _____ made of leather?

3. He was so worried that he was _____ in class.

4. What are you doing this _____?

5. After _____, I am planning to go to college.

6. She always wears red _____.

7. There are three swings at the new _____.

Form one compound for each word. Then add the definition of the compound.

First Word	Second Word	New Compound	Definition
winter	*break*	*winter break*	*a break during winter*
8. life			
9. paper			
10. color			
11. break			
12. any			
13. back			
14. traffic			
15. police			

Name _____ Date _____

REMEMBER When you read, connect ideas by following a three-step process. First, read the headings. Second, write notes on the main ideas under each heading as you read. Last, look over your notes after you are done reading. Ask yourself, "How are the ideas connected?"

Underline the heading for each paragraph. Read the paragraph. Then answer the questions.

Detectives Are Problem-Solvers
Art is stolen from a museum. An important person is kidnapped. A virus destroys files in a computer. Detectives are called in to solve these crimes, and many more like them. Some experts study fingerprints, handwriting, and tire tracks for clues. Other experts use new technologies to examine the evidence. But in the end, the detective has to put it all together. The detective has to solve the crime to help catch the criminals.

1. What is the main idea of this passage?

    _____

2. How is the main idea connected to the paragraph's heading?

    _____

    _____

Follow the Routine
When a crime is discovered, detectives are called to the scene. They start by closing the area. They put special yellow tape all around the place so the evidence will not be disturbed. The detectives collect evidence. They take photos of the crime scene. They sometimes use special film to show things they wouldn't otherwise be able to see. Every step of the detectives routine has to be followed in order. That way no evidence is overlooked.

3. What is the main idea of this passage?

    _____

4. How is the main idea connected to the paragraph's heading?

    _____

    _____

    _____

Choose the best answer for each item. Circle the letter of the correct answer.

1. It is true that fingerprints _____.

   a. do not help you grip   **b.** never change as you grow   **c.** are the same in twins

2. All fingerprints can be divided into three main groups: loops, whorls, and _____.

   a. arches   **b.** lines   **c.** squares

3. DNA samples from two unrelated people _____.

   a. are always the same   **b.** may match sometimes   **c.** will be different

4. In 1997, scientists used DNA to clone a _____.

   a. sheep   **b.** dinosaur   **c.** human being

5. Now computers can record your _____.

   a. personality   **b.** character   **c.** fingerprints

EXTENSION *Use with textbook page 139.*

In the left column, write five things that computers can record about you. In the right column, write how this information can be used.

What Computers Can Do	How This Information Can Be Used
voice patterns	prove who you are

GRAMMAR

Factual Conditionals: Present and Future *Use with textbook page 140.*

> **REMEMBER** A factual conditional in the present describes a fact that is always true. Use the simple present for both the *if* clause and the main clause. The factual conditional in the future describes future situations that have a real possibility of happening. Use the simple present for the *if* clause and the simple future (*will* + base verb) in the main clause.

Write *FCP* on the line if the sentences describe a fact that is always true (the factual conditional). Write *FCF* on the line if the sentences describe a situation that will probably happen (the future conditional).

_____ **1.** If it rains a lot, the plants will grow.

_____ **2.** If the water pollution is very bad, the fish will die.

_____ **3.** If the water is frozen, the temperature is below 32 degrees.

_____ **4.** If you are nice, people will like you.

_____ **5.** If a baby smiles, she or he is happy.

Complete the sentences with the verb in parentheses. Put the verbs in the correct tense.

6. (be) If the post office is closed, it _____ an official holiday.

7. (feel) If you smile, you _____ better.

8. (be) If the animal has a heartbeat, it _____ alive.

9. (have) If the warning light is on, you _____ a problem with the engine.

10. (want) If the cookies are burned, no one _____ any.

Write Instructions *Use with textbook page 141.*

This is the sequence chart that Kate completed before writing her paragraph.

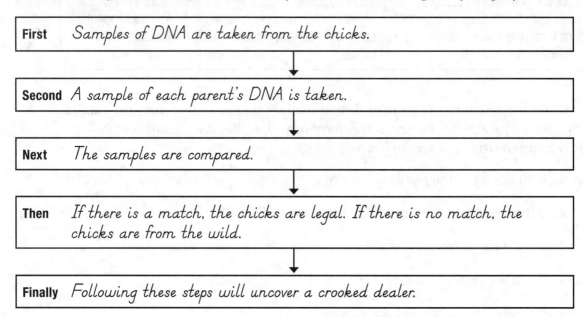

| First | *Samples of DNA are taken from the chicks.* |

| Second | *A sample of each parent's DNA is taken.* |

| Next | *The samples are compared.* |

| Then | *If there is a match, the chicks are legal. If there is no match, the chicks are from the wild.* |

| Finally | *Following these steps will uncover a crooked dealer.* |

Complete your own sequence chart that explains, step by step, how to identify who made a mystery print.

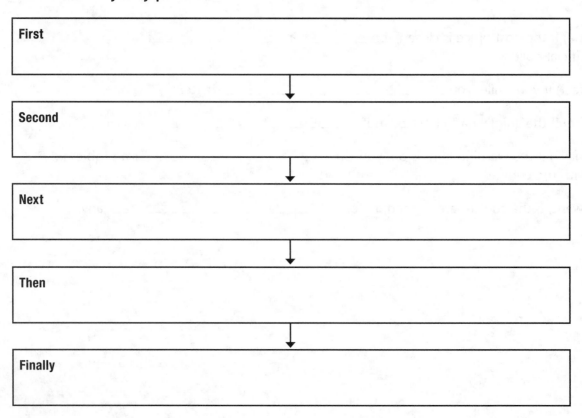

| First | |

| Second | |

| Next | |

| Then | |

| Finally | |

What shapes our identity?

READING 5: "Tears of Sorrow and Joy"

VOCABULARY **Decoding Strategies** *Use with textbook page 143.*

> **REMEMBER** A **digraph** is a pair of letters that come together to make one sound. For example, *ph* sounds the same as *f*. A **prefix** is a letter group that comes *before* a base word to give it new meaning. A **suffix** is a letter group that comes *after* a base word.

Look at the words below. Underline the pair of letters in each word that form a digraph.

Example: <u>ch</u>ampion

1. phone

2. shatter

3. steak

4. thumb

Look at the chart below. Write the prefix or suffix used in the word. Then write the meaning of the prefix or suffix.

Word	Prefix or Suffix	Meaning of prefix or suffix
Example: worthless	*less*	*without*
1. reinvent		
2. openness		
3. unreal		
4. disinherit		
5. stackable		

Use with textbook page 144.

> **REMEMBER** In the **first-person point of view,** the narrator is a character in the story. In the **third-person point of view**, the narrator is a voice that describes what happens in the story but does not participate in the action. The narrator's point of view affects *how* the story is told. Forms of narration often affect the tone of a work of fiction. The tone represents the writer's attitude toward the book's audience and subject.

The following paragraphs are written from different points of view. Label each paragraph *first person* or *third person*.

1.   The soccer players were all over the field. A mighty kick from the blue team sent the ball rocketing into the goal net. The hearts of every player on the yellow team sank like stones.

_____

2.   I couldn't believe I had lost my backpack. My house keys and cell phone were in it. My brother wasn't due home for hours and I had no idea what I was going to do until then.

_____

3.   Unfortunately, the students had become lost in the forest. Brady said, "Did anyone bring a cell phone?" Ernesto all looked at him incredulously and asked, "Seriously, what cell phone is going to work in the middle of a forest?"

_____

LITERARY ANALYSIS Elements of Fiction

Use with textbook page 145.

> **REMEMBER** All stories have a **plot**, or series of events and actions based on some type of problem or conflict. In the first part of a traditional plot structure, the author introduces the conflict and creates rising action. Eventually there is a climax, or turning point. This is the most intense moment of the story. In the end, the character's conflict is usually resolved during the falling action.

Reread the excerpt below from *Finding Miracles* in Unit 2. Decide whether the scene is part of the story's rising action or falling action. Refer back to the story in your textbook as needed. Then write how the scene contributes to the overall success of the plot.

From *Finding Miracles* by Julia Alvarez:

But then Mr. Barstow said something that made my hands begin to itch and my face darken with self-consciousness.

Em, my best friend, sits one row over and three seats in front of me. I could see her shoulders tense up. She was going to turn around any moment. *Please, Em,* I thought, *please don't!* I just couldn't stand her drawing any attention to me.

But if Em looked my way, I never knew. I stared down at the graffiti on my desk until it began to swim under my eyes, reorganizing into the shape of the country where Mr. Barstow had mentioned Pablo was from.

_____

_____

_____

_____

_____

Elements of Fiction
Use with textbook page 146.

REMEMBER Most stories contain some kind of **conflict**. There are two main kinds of conflicts that characters face. An internal conflict is a problem that exists within a character, such as a **moral dilemma**, confusion, fear, or uncertainty. An external conflict occurs when a character must deal with a problem involving outside forces, such as other people, nature, or weather.

Read the two summaries below. Then answer the questions.

Sophie's Choice (a novel by William Stryon, an American writer)

During World War II, Sophie Zawistowska and her two children are captured by the Nazis and taken to a concentration camp. The Nazi officers give her a choice: she can save one child, but not both. Sophie is tortured by the decision and thinks it may be best to lose them both rather than choose one over the other. But just as the Nazis carry away the boy and the girl, Sophie suddenly decides that it makes more sense to save the boy, who is more likely to survive. However, Sophie loses touch with her son and does not know whether he survives. She is haunted by her choice.

"Agamemnon" (a play by Aeschylus, an ancient Greek playwright)

In the beginning of the play, the audience learns that Agamemnon, the king of Argos, faced a moral dilemma before the start of the play. Agamemnon and his brother Menelaus decided to start a war against the Trojans after they kidnapped Menelaus's wife. As Agamemnon and his Greek ships are trying to sail to fight the Trojans, they encounter a problem: the ships cannot sail because Artemis, the goddess of the hunt, has stopped the winds. Artemis is punishing Agamemnon because he had recently bragged about killing a wild animal. Agamemnon has a choice: if he sacrifices his daughter Iphigenia, she will allow their ships to sail. Determined to fight the Trojans, Agamemnon chooses to sacrifice Iphigenia.

What moral dilemmas do Sophie and Agamemnon face? How are the dilemmas similar? How are they different?

_____

_____

_____

_____

GRAMMAR

Restrictive and Nonrestrictive Clauses *Use with textbook page 151.*

> **REMEMBER** A **restrictive clause** is a clause that is necessary to identify the word it modifies. A restrictive clause often begins with *who* or *that*. No commas are used to punctuate restrictive clauses. A **nonrestrictive clause** is a clause that is not necessary to identify the word it modifies. It just adds more information in the sentence. A nonrestrictive clause often begins with *who* or *which*. Sentences using nonrestrictive clauses are punctuated with commas.

Decide whether each sentence below contains a restrictive or nonrestrictive relative clause. Underline the clause and write *restrictive* or *nonrestrictive* on the lines below. Add commas where needed.

Example: The woman <u>who has brown hair</u> stole the car. _____*restrictive*_____

Example: Angela<u>, who is my cousin,</u> made the statewide track team. _____*nonrestrictive*_____

1. The teacher who has dark hair said that her favorite color is yellow.

_____

2. The window that has been broken twice is now broken again.

_____

3. The hip-hop star who is rather tall has sold many albums.

_____

4. The party which was planned for Saturday will now be on Sunday.

_____

5. Add the ingredients for the cake mix which is on the counter.

_____

6. The student who has the highest grade won the prize.

_____

7. The birdhouse that sits in the oak tree has been invaded by squirrels.

_____

8. Your homework which seems impossible can be completed with hard work.

_____

> **REMEMBER** A well-told **short story** should contain a variety of literary elements. It needs a developed, suspenseful plot based on interesting, believable characters and a conflict. The author should provide sensory details and dialogue that help readers understand the characters and their situations.

Use this chart to help generate ideas about your characters and conflict. Write your ideas on the lines.

CHARACTER and CONFLICT

Who is your main character? What details can you include about your main character that will help the reader understand the character's personality and situation?

_____

_____

How would the main character realistically speak?

_____

_____

What conflict does this character face? Is it an external or internal conflict? (Remember, your story can have both.)

_____

_____

How will the conflict be resolved?

_____

_____

What other characters will appear in the story? What are their personalities?

_____

_____

WRITING

Write what will happen at each stage of your short story in the chart below.

PRODUCE A MULTIMEDIA PRESENTATION

Gather and Organize Information *Use with textbook page 156.*

This is an outline that lists the images and sounds for the introduction to a presentation on making *Tears of Sorrow and Joy* into a movie.

Speaker	Music	Image on Computer Screen
Hi, we're here to tell you why a great short story can become an even greater movie.	*Ragtime piano or Dixieland jazz*	Photo of New Orleans in the 1880s
The story is about a modern teen who discovers her New Orleans roots through a letter written by an ancestor.	*Sound effects: rain on window*	Modern girl reading old letter
The story will appeal to a lot of people because we all want to belong to something bigger than ourselves.	*Quiet pop song*	Modern girl talking with grandmother

Complete your own outline for the introduction to a presentation on making your short story into a movie.

Speaker	Music	Image on Computer Screen

EDIT AND PROOFREAD   *Use with textbook page 164.*

Read the paragraph carefully. Look for mistakes in spelling, punctuation, and grammar. Correct the mistakes with the editing marks on Student Book page 563. Then rewrite the paragraph correctly on the lines below.

> My family and i do many fun things together. Sometimes we visit our freinds and relatives who live near and far. Other times, we have a picnic by the lake and play baseball. we reelly like to go camping together. We go to many speshul places like state parks. When you are camping, you have to know what to do. My brother Marco is great at camping. He could set up the tent because he does it every year. He can even bake a cake over the campfire My father likes to toast marshmallows over the Campfire. My mother enjoy watching birds. If the weather is good, we will camp agen next week.

_____

_____

_____

_____

_____

_____

_____

_____

_____

_____

Underline the vocabulary items you know and can use well. Review and practice any you haven't underlined. Underline them when you know them well.

Literary Words	Key Words		Academic Words	
conflict	character traits	biometric	adapt	achieve
point of view	empathy	captivity	conflict	adequate
theme	influences	data bank	identity	construct
suspense	inventory	genetic	interpret	culture
	relationships	laser	issue	emphasis
	tolerant	technologies	reveal	perception
	authorized		adult	distinctive
			attitude	evidence
			categories	identical
			communication	identification
			manipulating	invisible
			response	visible

Put a check by the skills you can perform well. Review and practice any you haven't checked off. Check them off when you can perform them well.

Skills	I can . . .
Word Study	☐ recognize and spell words with diphthongs /ou/ and /oi/. ☐ recognize and use collocations with *make* and *take*. ☐ recognize and spell words with long *a*. ☐ recognize and use compound words. ☐ recognize and use decoding strategies.
Reading Strategies	☐ recognize cause and effect.　　☐ identify author's purpose. ☐ classify.　　☐ connect ideas.
Grammar	☐ use modals for ability, possibility, or necessity. ☐ use *would* + *rather* + verb and unreal conditional. ☐ use *have to* + verb for necessity, *supposed to be* + verb for expectation. ☐ use factual conditionals: present and future. ☐ use restrictive and nonrestrictive relative clauses.
Writing	☐ explain the steps in a process. ☐ explain how something is classified. ☐ write a cause-and-effect paragraph. ☐ write instructions. ☐ write a short story. ☐ write an expository essay.

Visual Literacy: Smithsonian American
Art Museum *Use with textbook pages 166–167.*

INTERPRETATION

Look at *A Matter of Trust* by Maria Castagliola on page 166 in your textbook. The artist asked friends and family to write secrets down on pieces of paper. She sealed those secrets in envelopes and then sewed the envelopes into this work of art.

Pretend you can see through one of the envelopes and read one of the secrets. Write what you imagine that secret to be.

Example: *I just moved and I miss my old friends.*

_____

_____

_____

_____

LETTER

Next, write a letter to the author of the secret that either advises them on a plan of action or consoles them in some way.

Dear _____,

_____

_____

_____

_____

_____

Look at *El Chandelier* by Pepón Osorio on page 167 in your textbook. Use that artwork to complete the Web Diagram below. For each "string" coming from the center, list one observation about the artwork.

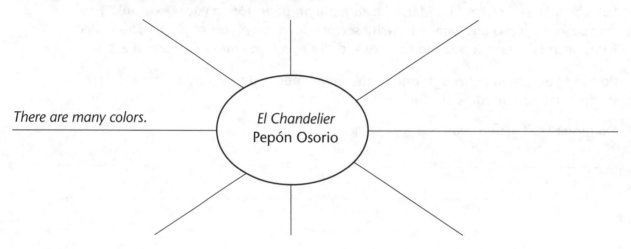

There are many colors.

El Chandelier
Pepón Osorio

Look at *El Chandelier* by Pepón Osorio on page 167 in your textbook. Answer these questions.

K	W	L	H
What do you **know** about using everyday objects in art?	What do you **want** to learn about this work of art?	What have you **learned** about the way some artists use everyday objects in art?	**How** did you learn it?

Now that you have read about mixed identities, go to www.LongmanKeystone.com for links to the Smithsonian website. Follow the online instructions to compare the artwork in your student book with other media that convey similar messages. Which messages are conveyed more directly through visual media? Which ideas are conveyed more effectively through print or audio?

When should you take a stand?

READING 1: From *going going*

VOCABULARY **Literary Words** *Use with textbook page 171.*

> **REMEMBER** **Hyperbole** is deliberate exaggeration used for effect. **Example:** My suitcase weighs about 1,000 pounds.
> **Dialogue** is speech or conversation between characters in a story. **Example:** "I saw you at the cafe yesterday," she said.

Read the sentences. Write whether the sentences describe examples of hyperbole or dialogue.

Example: ___*dialogue*___ "Stop playing your drums when I'm trying to study!" yelled Sharise.

1. _____ I think of you a million times a day.

2. _____ "Are you coming or not?" asked Dameon. "Well, I guess so," said Marc.

3. _____ My history teacher is so old—he must have lived through most of the events in our history textbook!

4. _____ Jerome is so tall; we worry that his head will knock the sun out of the sky.

5. _____ "Did you see our teacher today?" whispered Bette to Ramon.

Read the passage. Circle examples of hyperbole. Underline examples of dialogue.

> Elizabeth was so hungry she could have eaten a horse. "When is lunch?" she asked her Mom. Mrs. Sanchez smiled at Elizabeth and said, "It will be ready in just a few minutes." After lunch, Elizabeth had a stomachache. She had eaten a ton. Her eyes were always larger than her stomach.

Read the paragraph below. Pay attention to the underlined academic words.

> Miko's, a local eating establishment, was being threatened by a big restaurant chain. Construction had begun across the street from Miko's. In previous cases, local restaurants had shut down when this chain restaurant moved into a neighborhood. Louise was upset that she might no longer have access to her favorite restaurant. She disliked chain restaurants on principle because she believed they ruined small businesses. Plus, she loved the taste of Miko's food. When Louise discovered that others in the community were upset, she organized a protest march.

Match each word with its definition.

Example: ___*b*___ principle

_____ **1.** previous

_____ **2.** construction

_____ **3.** community

_____ **4.** access

_____ **5.** establishment

a. a group of people who live in the same town or area

b. a moral rule or set of ideas that makes you behave in a particular way

c. an institution, especially a business, store, or hotel

d. the right to enter a place, use something, or see something

e. the process of building something, such as a house or road

f. happening or existing before a particular event, time, or thing

Use the academic words from the exercise above to complete the sentences.

6. This ticket gives me _____ to the backstage area after the concert.

7. Many workers were involved in the _____ of the new building.

8. The neighborhood pool is a fun place for members of our _____ to meet.

Complete the sentences with your own ideas.

Example: One establishment I enjoy visiting is *the restaurant down the street*.

9. An important principle to live by is _____.

10. The students in the previous class _____.

WORD STUDY   **Homophones** *Use with textbook page 173.*

> **REMEMBER** Homophones are two or more words that sound the same but have different spellings and meanings.
> **Examples:** *knight/night; pair/pear*

Complete the sentences with the correct homophone from the parentheses.

Example: (night/knight) My _____*knight*_____ in shining armor came riding in on a white horse.

1. (some/sum) The _____ of 12 + 5 is 17.

2. (groan/grown) My son has _____ out of all his clothes during the summer.

3. (jeans/genes) I really like my new blue_____.

4. (principal/principle) The _____ of our school is a great leader.

5. (peek/peak) Can I take a _____ at the picture?

6. (sighs/size) What _____ shoes do you wear?

7. (pores/pours) When it rains, it _____!

Circle the homophone that fits the description.

Example: (you use your ears to do this) here/(hear)

8. (more than one) two/to

9. (a large furry animal) bare/bear

10. (it flies in the air) plain/plane

11. (you'll probably see one at Halloween) witch/which

12. (thieves do this) steel/steal

13. (the same as sixty minutes) hour/our

14. (you use it to make bread) flour/flower

15. (another word for *slice*) piece/peace

Use with textbook page 173.

> **REMEMBER** Facts are true statements. Facts can be proved by checking in books or other sources. Opinions are what people think or believe about something. It is the reader's job to evaluate which is which.

Read the sentences. Write whether the sentences describe facts or opinions.

Example: _____opinion_____ Chocolate cake is the best kind of cake there is.

1. _____ Chocolate is made out of pods from the cacao tree.

2. _____ The fruit of the cacao tree looks very strange.

3. _____ A cacao pod can weigh between 200 and 800 grams.

4. _____ Two-thirds of the world's cocoa is produced in Africa.

5. _____ There are many interesting places to visit in Africa.

Read this paragraph. Circle the opinions and underline the facts.

Long ago, flat breads called "pizzas" were sold all over Italy. These breads had no toppings, but were eaten plain. In the late 1800s, Queen Margherita sampled some pizza bread. It was delicious! Some people thought she shouldn't eat the same type of bread that poor people ate. The queen didn't care. She asked a chef named Rafaelle to bake pizzas for her. Rafaelle was devoted to his queen. To honor the queen, he made a pizza with tomatoes, mozzarella cheese, and basil to show the red, white, and green of the Italian flag. Pizza as we know it was born. In my opinion, it's the most delectable food in the world!

Name _____ Date _____

Choose the best answer for each item. Circle the letter of the correct answer.

1. Florrie's birthday wish was for her family to _____.

   a. stop fighting
   and spend
   time together

   b. only shop at independent
   businesses for the
   rest of the year

   c. make a donation to a
   charity that helps
   small business owners

2. True feels that Florrie's wish shows that she is _____.

   a. kind

   b. heroic

   c. bossy

3. An example of Florrie's use of hyperbole is _____.

   a. "We have to do
   this: we have
   no choice!"

   b. "We can make a
   few exceptions
   if necessary."

   c. "That equals sixteen
   weeks, one week for
   each year of my life."

4. From the dialogue in this story, you can tell that Ruben _____.

   a. is very shy and
   quiet

   b. doesn't want to hurt
   his sister's feelings

   c. agrees with his
   sister's idea

5. Something that helps Della form an opinion about Florrie's idea is _____.

   a. her father used to
   support
   independent
   businesses

   b. she buys from
   different businesses
   for her restaurant

   c. she is too busy to worry
   about whether a
   business is
   independent or not

Florrie believes very strongly in something. What is something that you believe is very important? Write a paragraph about it. Explain why other people should care about it, too.

_____

_____

_____

_____

_____

GRAMMAR

Used to + Verb and Would + Verb for Habit in the Past

Use with textbook page 182.

REMEMBER To talk about habits in the past that do not continue in the present, use *used to* + the base form of a verb or *would* + the base form of a verb.

Complete the sentences with phrases from the box.

used to eat	would say	used to be	would wear	used to go

1. When my mother was a child, people _____ white clothing only during the summer.

2. Before he was a lawyer, my father _____ a mechanic.

3. The baby _____ "Baba" instead of "Daddy."

4. My family _____ to the beach every summer.

5. My friend _____ meat, but now she is a vegetarian.

Rewrite the verbs in the sentences to express a habit in the past. Follow the directions in parentheses.

Example: My grandmother plays the violin.

(Use *would*.) My grandmother _would play_ the violin.

6. They write poems.

(Use *used to*.) They _____ poems.

7. The men catch fish in that stream.

(Use *would*.) The men _____ fish in that stream.

8. The comedians tell that joke every year.

(Use *would*.) The comedians _____ that joke every year.

9. We laugh every time.

(Use *used to*.) We _____ every time.

10. The farmers grow corn.

(Use *used to*.) The farmers _____ corn.

86

WRITING

Write an Advertisement *Use with textbook page 183.*

This is the T-chart that Jack completed before writing his paragraph.

Used to	Now
be greeted by name	*no one knows you*
stores sold food and clothing at low prices	*coffee is five dollars instead of one dollar*

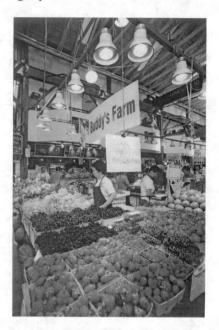

Complete your own T-chart for an ad, brochure, or commercial about a cause that you believe in. List details for *Used to* and *Now*.

Used to	Now

When should you take a stand?

READING 2: From *Freedom Walkers: The Story of the Montgomery Bus Boycott*

VOCABULARY **Key Words** *Use with textbook page 185.*

Write each word from the box next to its definition below.

accustomed	entitled	offense	official	privilege	protested	vacated

Example: ___*vacated*___: left a seat, room, etc., so that someone else could use it

1. _____: something that is wrong; a crime

2. _____: having the right to have or do something

3. _____: approved of or done by someone in authority, especially the government

4. _____: displayed disapproval by an individual or group towards something that is wrong or unfair

5. _____: a special advantage given to one person or group of people

6. _____: used to; in the habit of

Use the words from the box at the top of the page to complete the sentences.

7. After the family _____ the apartment, we were able to move in.

8. We _____ the war by marching with signs.

9. I believe that every child is _____ to a good education.

10. We have to follow the _____ rules of the game, as written by its national organization.

VOCABULARY **Academic Words** *Use with textbook page 186.*

Read the paragraph. Pay attention to the underlined academic words.

In 1955, seats at the front of many buses in the South were <u>restricted</u> to whites. Rosa Parks was <u>occupying</u> a seat behind the whites-only section on a Montgomery, Alabama bus. When the bus filled up, the driver said she had to move so white people could sit. Ms. Parks refused to move. Under the official <u>policy</u> of Montgomery, she wasn't <u>required</u> to move, and she was not <u>violating</u> the law. Still, she was arrested. Rosa Parks later worked to help make freedom from racial discrimination a <u>constitutional</u> right.

Write the academic words from the paragraph above next to their correct definitions.

Example: ___*policy*___: a way of doing things that has been officially agreed upon and chosen by a political party, business, or organization

1. _____: officially allowed or restricted by a government's set of rules

2. _____: disobeying or doing something against a law, rule, agreement, etc.

3. _____: something that must be done because of a rule or law

4. _____: filling a particular amount of space

5. _____: controlled or limited

Use the academic words from the exercise above to complete the sentences.

6. The police stopped the driver who was _____ the speed limit.

7. You need special permission to go into areas that are _____.

8. Many people fought against the _____ of making African Americans ride in the back of buses.

Complete the sentences with your own ideas.

Example: All U. S. citizens have the constitutional right to ___*free speech*___.

9. Something that you are required to do in school is

_____.

10. If someone is occupying your seat on an airplane,

_____.

REMEMBER The long *i* sound can be spelled several different ways. These include *i_e* as in *side*, *ai* as in *aisle*, *igh* as in *tight*, *y* as in *my* and *i* as in *kind*. Knowing these patterns helps you notice the inflections (endings) on a word.

Read the words in the box below. Then write each word in the correct column in the chart.

smile	imply	isle	delighted	while	justify
grind	tightly	slime	blind	lightning	goodbye

Words with long *i* spelled *i_e*	Words with long *i* spelled *igh*	Words with long *i* spelled *y*	Words with long *i* spelled *i*
smile			

Write the letter-sound pattern in each word below.

Example: might ___long i spelled igh___

12. island _____

13. find _____

14. slice _____

15. simplify _____

16. price _____

17. sigh _____

18. rind _____

19. unify _____

20. flight _____

READING STRATEGY | **RECOGNIZE SEQUENCE** | *Use with textbook page 187.*

> **REMEMBER** Sequence is the order in which things happen. When you read, try to keep track of the order of events. Words that can help you follow the sequence in a text include: *first, next, then, before, after,* and *finally.* Dates will also help you see the order in which events happen.

Read the paragraph. Then answer the questions below.

> Diego Rivera was one of the most famous Mexican artists in the world. When he was ten, he began attending an art school in Mexico City. He studied there for seven years. Then he received money from the government to study art in Europe. Diego first studied in Spain, and then he went to Paris, France. He became a successful painter there. Soon, he saw that only rich people could afford to buy his paintings. He wanted everyone to see his art. He studied mural painting, or the art of painting on walls. After living in Europe, Diego went back to Mexico and painted on public walls, where everyone could see his work. Over the years, Diego painted over 100 murals on the walls of buildings in Mexico and the United States.

1. Underline the words that help you keep track of the order of events.

2. How old was Diego Rivera when he started attending art school?

   _____

3. What did Diego Rivera do after he attended art school in Mexico City?

   _____

4. Where did Diego move after living in Europe?

   _____

5. Reread the paragraph. Fill in this timeline to show some of the events in the order that they happened.

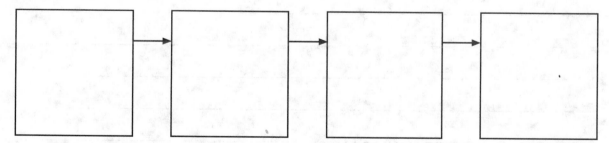

Choose the best answer for each item. Circle the letter of the correct answer.

1. This article tells about African-American teenagers who _____.

    a. walked to school every day

    b. fought for their constitutional rights

    c. agreed to sit in the back of the bus

2. In Alabama, Edwina and Marshall Johnson sat in the white section of the bus

   because _____.

    a. they wanted to resist the law

    b. they didn't know the law

    c. it was their constitutional right

3. After she was arrested, Claudette Colvin felt _____.

    a. scared

    b. embarrassed

    c. angry

4. People were surprised that Claudette was judged to be guilty because _____.

    a. she didn't break any laws

    b. she yelled at the police officer

    c. she usually behaved very well

5. All of the events in this passage happened _____.

    a. after Rosa Parks refused to give up her seat on a bus

    b. before Rosa Parks refused to give up her seat on a bus

    c. before buses were divided into white and black sections

EXTENSION *Use with textbook page 193.*

Did you ever not obey a rule because you felt it was wrong? Write a paragraph to tell about why you felt the rule was wrong, and what happened when you disobeyed it.

_____

_____

_____

_____

Name _____ Date _____

Simple Past *Use with textbook page 194.*

> **REMEMBER** Use the simple past for actions that started and ended in the past. The past of regular verbs is formed by adding *-d*, *-ed*, or *-ied*. The form is the same for all persons. The past of irregular verbs often looks different from the base form.

Complete the chart with words from the box.

became	liked	hurried	rang	slept
clapped	ate	clicked	stood	studied

Base Form	Simple Past	Base Form	Simple Past
1. ring		**6.** stand	
2. eat		**7.** click	
3. clap		**8.** become	
4. sleep		**9.** study	
5. like		**10.** hurry	

Write sentences with the verbs in parentheses. Put the verbs in the simple past.

Example: (be) *He was in my class last year.*

11. (hum) _____

_____

12. (be) _____

_____

13. (remember) _____

_____

14. (fly) _____

_____

15. (marry) _____

_____

Write a Critique *Use with textbook page 195.*

This is the word web that Chas completed before writing his paragraph.

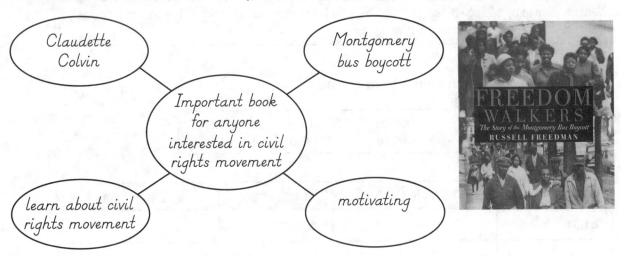

Complete your own word web about the excerpt from *Freedom Walkers*. List your main point and strong phrases, opinion phrases, and supporting details.

Name _____ Date _____

UNIT 3 When should you take a stand?

READING 3: "The Ravine"

VOCABULARY **Literary Words** *Use with textbook page 197.*

REMEMBER The **plot** is the sequence of the events in a story. Individual scenes contribute to the plot. A **flashback** is a reference to something that happened earlier. **Character motivation** is the reason why a character behaves, speaks, or thinks in a certain way.

Read the sentences. Label whether the sentences contain information regarding *plot, character motivation,* **or a** *flashback*.

Example: First, Jane runs away. Then her parents find her. After a long talk, they convince her to come home.

_____ *plot* _____

1. James wanted to be a musician.

   _____

2. It reminded her of that morning several years ago. It had been a sunny day and the sunlight had glittered on the bay.

   _____

3. Alice was perfectly happy until her family decided to share their house with another family. First the family started crowding her out of the living room. Then Alice had to share her bedroom with another girl. At last, her parents asked the family to move out.

   _____

4. Joan worked hard because she wanted to make her parents proud.

   _____

Read the paragraph. Circle examples of flashback. Underline clues about motivation.

5.   Jack was determined to make the baseball team. Jack was scared. All he could think about was what happened last year. At last year's tryouts, he swung at every pitch. He struck out. He could still remember the disappointed look on the coach's face. He could still remember how hot and red his face had become with embarrassment. This year would be different. Jack was completely focused on making the team.

Read the paragraph below. Pay attention to the underlined academic words.

Ryan was in a car accident last winter. Strong winds and an icy bridge were the circumstances that led to the accident. Ryan's car slid across the ice and hit the side rail of the bridge. Ryan was very lucky. The accident didn't badly injure him, and he suffered no internal damage. Later, Ryan took the time to reconstruct what had happened. He realized he should have been able to predict there would be ice on the bridge, and should have driven more slowly. The accident had an affect on Ryan by making him a more careful driver.

Match each word with its definition.

Example: __c__ predict

_____ 1. circumstances

_____ 2. affect

_____ 3. internal

_____ 4. reconstruct

_____ 5. injure

a. inside something, such as your body

b. the facts or conditions that affect a situation, action, event, etc.

c. foretell

d. construct or enact again

e. do something that produces a change in someone or something; influence

f. hurt a person or animal

Use the academic words from the exercise above to complete the sentences.

6. By asking lots of questions, the reporter tried to _____ what happened at the community meeting.

7. Scary movies _____ people in different ways; some people have nightmares, and others are not bothered at all.

8. If you lift those heavy chairs, you might _____ your back.

Complete the sentences with your own ideas.

Example: When we are children, one rule we learn is that under no circumstances should we *talk to strangers* .

9. I predict that tomorrow _____.

10. An example of an internal organ is _____.

Name _____ Date _____

REMEMBER Words that derive from verbs and end in *-ed* or *-ing* follow a few specific spelling rules. One of the rules is that the final consonant is doubled if the base form of the verb has a short vowel sound followed by a consonant, unless the base verb already has a double consonant.
Examples: *chat/chatting; rob/robbed;* but *tell/telling*
If the word has a long vowel sound and ends in *-e*, drop the *-e* before adding *-ed* or *-ing.*
Examples: *make/making; bake/baked*

Complete the chart by adding the word forms ending in *-ed* and *-ing*.

	-ed	-ing
talk	*talked*	*talking*
1. hate		
2. hug		
3. move		
4. live		
5. shop		
6. disappear		

Complete the chart with nine other words ending in *-ed* or *-ing*. Include at least one word in each category.

-ed	-ing
hummed	**11.**
7.	**12.**
8.	**13.**
9.	**14.**
10.	**15.**

REMEMBER When you read, try to predict or guess what will happen, in a story. You can do this by asking yourself, "What will happen next?" When you predict, look for clues in the story and in the illustrations. Think about what you already know about the topic.

Read the paragraphs. Then answer the questions below.

1. I stood quietly at the edge of the pool. I looked around and saw all of my friends laughing and splashing and having a great time. Why had I agreed to come to Andrew's pool party? I hate to swim.

    "What are you waiting for? Jump in!" shouted Sasha.

    What do you predict will happen?

    _____

2. "No, I think I'll just go get a soda," I said, trying to sound cool.

    "A soda?" laughed Jerome. "That won't cool you off as much as a nice swim in the pool. Jump in! Or I'll come out and give you a push!"

    What do you predict will happen?

    _____

3. I took two steps away from the pool. I couldn't help it. I started to cry.

    "Are those tears?" asked Jerome. "Are you scared or something?"

    What do you predict will happen?

    _____

4. I just stood there, frozen. Sasha came out of the pool and wrapped herself in a large, blue towel. "We're both going to get a soda," she said to Jerome. Sasha took me aside. "Is everything okay? What's bothering you?"

    What do you predict will happen?

    _____

5. I burst into tears. "Sasha, I'm so embarrassed. I hate to swim. I shouldn't have come."

    "Shhh," said Sasha. "It's fine. There are a lot of things you can do at a pool party besides swimming. You can just spend time with your friends, talk, and have fun."

    What do you predict will happen?

    _____

COMPREHENSION *Use with textbook page 208.*

Choose the best answer for each item. Circle the letter of the correct answer.

1. Vinny thinks they shouldn't be in the ravine because _____.

   a. a boy had disappeared after jumping off the waterfall

   b. Starlene had been daring him to jump into it

   c. Vinny wanted to climb up the trail to the top of the waterfall

2. Vinny believes that jumping off the waterfall is _____.

   a. fun　　　　　　**b.** dangerous　　　　　　**c.** easy

3. Vinny thinks he has no choice but to jump because _____.

   a. he doesn't want his friends to think he is scared

   b. he needs to know what happened to the dead boy

   c. he has to rescue Joe-Boy

4. As Vinny climbs up to the ledge, you can predict that _____.

   a. he will fall　　　　**b.** he will find the dead boy　　　**c.** he will jump

5. At the end of the story, Vinny _____.

   a. jumps into the ravine　　**b.** walks down the trail　　**c.** rescues his friend

RESPONSE TO LITERATURE *Use with textbook page 209.*

Think about Vinny's decision at the end of the story. Write a paragraph about a time when you felt you needed to prove something to your friends. How were your actions the same or different from Vinny's actions?

_____

_____

_____

_____

_____

_____

GRAMMAR

Reported Speech *Use with textbook page 210.*

REMEMBER In reported speech, use *told* when you mention the listener. Use *said* when you don't. Use *had to* (the past of *have to*) + the base form of a verb to show that an action was necessary.

Look at the following sentences. Write the sentences as reported speech in the space provided next to them.

Quoted Speech	Reported Speech
Sally said to Jim, "I am bored."	*Sally told Jim she was bored.*
1. I said to him "The book is mine."	
2. He said, "Use this door."	
3. I said to her, "I'm not ready."	
4. She said, "We have to leave."	
5. He said to her, "I hated the movie."	

Rewrite the quoted speeches as reported speeches.

Example: He said, "Take the dog for a walk."

　　He said to take the dog for a walk.

6. She said, "Remember to be polite."

_____

7. I said, "I have to stop at the library."

_____

8. We said to her, "You have to come with us."

_____

9. She said to him, "Sing with me."

_____

10. He told me, "You are funny."

_____

WRITING

Write a Personal Letter *Use with textbook page 211.*

This is the graphic organizer that Nola completed before writing her paragraph.

July 25, 2009

Dear Mom,

went to the ravine and almost jumped
I was scared because it was dangerous
friends tried to pressure me
remembered what you told me about the pond
had the courage not to jump

Love,
Vinny

Complete your own graphic organizer for an informal letter from Vinny to his mom, his dad, or one of his friends. List phrases that will win the person over so he or she understands why Vinny did not jump.

_____

_____ ,

_____ ,

_____

When should you take a stand?

READING 4: "Speak Your Mind"

VOCABULARY **Key Words** *Use with textbook page 213.*

Write each word from the box next to its definition below.

| apathy | blog | Congress | petition | protest |

Example: ____*apathy*____: the feeling of not being interested in something or not caring about life

1. _____: the group of people elected to make laws for the United States, consisting of the Senate and the House of Representatives

2. _____: a display of disapproval by an individual or group towards something that is wrong or unfair

3. _____: a piece of paper that asks someone in authority to do or change something, and is signed by many people

4. _____: an online diary or journal that anyone can read

Use the words from the box at the top of the page to complete the sentences.

5. It is a great honor to be elected to _____.

6. After school I like to go online and update my _____.

7. The workers gathered to _____ against their low wages and long hours.

8. Hundreds of people signed the _____ to keep the hospital open.

9. Because of the student's _____, he did very poorly in school.

10. A new law to protect the environment was approved by _____.

VOCABULARY   **Academic Words** *Use with textbook page 214.*

Read the paragraph below. Pay attention to the underlined academic words.

A forest near our house was threatened by a construction project. My sister became an underlined activist to try to save the forest. She decided to start her own underlined publication to inform people about the threat. Her one-page newspaper was an effective way to underlined communicate with the public. Many people read her paper, and she raised a great deal of underlined public awareness. Because of my sister's efforts, at the next underlined election many people voted for a candidate who opposed the construction.

Write the academic words from the paragraph next to their correct definitions.

Example: __*public awareness*__: common knowledge about a social or political issue

1. _____: a process by which people decide who will represent them
   in government

2. _____: a book, magazine, etc.

3. _____: a person who performs some kind of action in an effort to
   gain social or political change

4. _____: exchange information

Use the academic words from the exercise above to complete the sentences.

5. Our class holds _____ so that we can vote for the student we want
   to be class president.

6. I just read a _____ about new ways to save water.

7. The museum is trying to raise _____ about the importance of
   art education.

Complete the sentences with your own ideas.

Example: The activist let people know about her cause by __*giving a speech*__.

8. One publication I enjoy is _____.

9. Something I use to communicate with my friends and family is

   _____.

10. I think there should be more public awareness about _____.

REMEMBER The long /oo/ sound can be spelled and pronounced several different ways. These include *o* as in *to*, *u_e* as in *dude*, *ough* as in *through*, *oo* as in *snooze*, and *ou* as in *croup*. It can also be spelled *o* as in *so*, *u_e* as in *cure*, *ue* as in *argue*, *ough* as in *though*, *oo* as in *cook*, and *ou* as *about*. Knowing these patterns helps you spell and say the words correctly.

Read the words in the box below. Then write each word in the correct column in the chart.

to	through	doubt	took	ghoul	argue
lure	dough	so	drool	blue	nude

long /oo/ spelled *o*	long /oo/ spelled *u_e*	long /oo/ spelled *ue*
to	**3.**	**7.**
BUT	BUT	BUT
so	**4.**	**8.**
long /oo/ spelled *ough*	**long /oo/ spelled *oo***	**long /oo/ spelled *ou***
1.	**5.**	**9.**
BUT	BUT	BUT
2.	**6.**	**10.**

Write the letter-sound pattern in each word below.

Example: colt ___*long /oo/ spelled o*___

11. dude _____

12. sue _____

13. bough _____

14. fool _____

15. croup _____

READING STRATEGY EVALUATE NEW INFORMATION

Use with textbook page 215.

> **REMEMBER** When you evaluate new information, you connect it to information you already know. Doing so helps you to understand a text more easily.

Suppose you are assigned to write a report on blueberries. Your teacher asks you to use a reliable source written by an author who is a scientist. Read the paragraph and answer the questions.

1. Before you read the paragraph below, write what you already know about blueberries.

   _____

   > Blueberries are rich in nutrients, yet low in calories. Researchers at Tufts University have found that blueberries have a wide range of medicinal qualities. Eating blueberries can help prevent eye problems, heart disease, and cancer. In studies on animals, it was found that eating blueberries caused older animals' brains to function as well as those of younger animals. Researchers believe that blueberries might help brain problems in humans, too.

2. Was there information in the paragraph that you already knew? If so, write it below.

   _____

3. What information was completely new to you?

   _____

4. Does the new information help you understand the subject better? Why or why not?

   _____

5. In the space below, draw a T-chart. Show what you now know and what you would still like to learn about blueberries.

Choose the best answer for each item. Circle the letter of the correct answer.

1. The main point of this article is to urge kids to _____.

   a. get involved in issues   **b.** change the voting age   **c.** form a picket line

2. One way to communicate directly with a politician is to _____.

   a. send an e-mail   **b.** write a newspaper   **c.** sign a petition

3. A person who CANNOT vote in this year's election is _____.

   a. a man   **b.** a woman   **c.** a sixteen-year-old

4. The first step in organizing a protest is to _____.

   a. create a slogan   **b.** give people information   **c.** yell at people who
      for your cause   about the issue   disagree with you

5. When writing a letter to a politician with whom you disagree you should _____.

   a. use a nasty tone   **b.** be very emotional   **c.** be respectful

EXTENSION *Use with textbook page 221.*

Think about an issue in your community, state, or country that is important to you. Write a paragraph in which you explain your position on the issue.

_____

_____

_____

_____

_____

_____

_____

GRAMMAR

Passive Form of Modals: *should* + *be* + Past Participle

Use with textbook page 222.

> **REMEMBER** When an action is more important than the doer of the action, use the passive voice. To stress an action in the passive voice, use *should be* + the past participle of a verb. The past participle of a regular verb is formed by adding -*d* or -*ed*. There are many irregular past participles.

Complete the sentences with *should be, should not be,* or *shouldn't be* + the verb in parentheses. Use the verb in the correct form.

Example: (say) Nothing ___*should be said*___ once the test has begun.

1. (eat) The cookies _____ before dinner.

2. (number) The sentences _____ from 1 to 5.

3. (welcome) The new student _____ to the class.

4. (open) The gift _____ before your birthday.

5. (leave) Your bicycle _____ outside in the rain.

Write sentences with *should be, should not be,* or *shouldn't be* + the verb in parentheses. Use the verb in the correct form.

Example: (correct)

___*All errors should be corrected before your homework is submitted.*___

6. (speak)

_____

7. (allow)

_____

8. (increase)

_____

9. (copy)

_____

10. (send)

_____

Write a Letter to the Editor *Use with textbook page 223.*

This is the word web that Andrew completed before writing his paragraph.

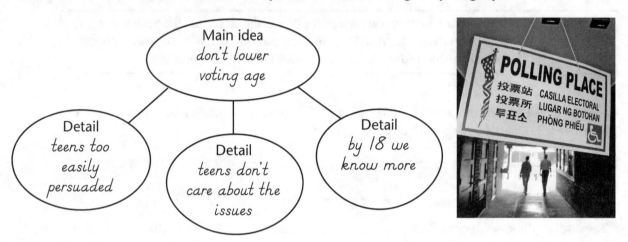

Complete your own word web about whether or not the voting age should be lowered. List your main idea and details.

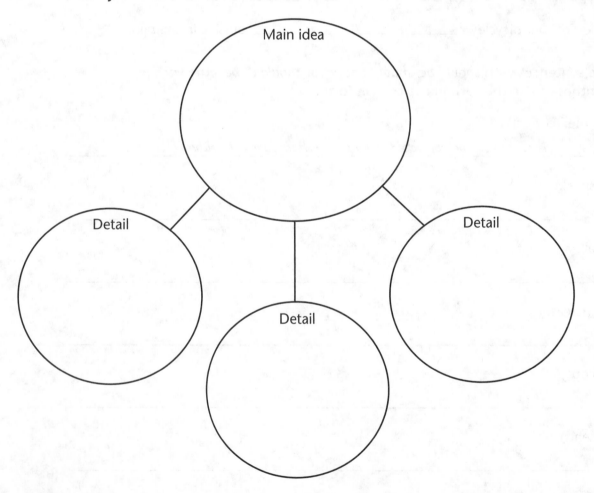

When should you take a stand?

READING 5: "Graduated Driver's License Program" / "Music in the Cafeteria"

VOCABULARY **Cognates** *Use with textbook page 225.*

REMEMBER Cognates are words that are related because they share a common etymology, or word origin. True cognates have the same or nearly the same meaning.

Look at the chart below. Write a cognate for each English word in the chart.

English Word and Meaning	Etymology, or Origin	Cognate
president = executive leader	from the Latin *praesidēre,* meaning "preside" or "act as authority over"	
mountain = very high rise of land	from the Latin *montaneus,* meaning "of a mountain"	
person = human being	from the Greek *prosōpon,* meaning "face, mask"	

Read the following sentences. Use the chart above and your knowledge of cognates to determine what each underlined word means.

1. The <u>presidential</u> race took a toll on the candidates. _____

2. The <u>mountaineer</u> reached the peak in record time. _____

3. We enjoyed meeting Tasha's <u>personable</u> friend. _____

4. During her <u>presidency</u>, Leigh tried to be fair. _____

5. The land was <u>mountainous</u> rather than flat. _____

6. The <u>personnel</u> office is responsible for the payroll. _____

Author's Purpose; Controlling Idea and Details *Use with textbook page 226.*

> **REMEMBER** An **author's purpose** is his or her reason for writing. Authors have many different motives for writing. Authors also develop a controlling idea related to their purpose. The **controlling idea** is usually supported by the **details** they include.

Read the following passages. Determine whether the author is writing to inform, entertain, or persuade. Then restate the controlling idea of the passage and the most important supporting details.

Passage	Author's Purpose	Controlling Idea	Supporting Details
Being a star runner isn't a requirement to babysit my three-year-old brother, but believe me, it helps. He's small, but he's fast—really fast. In just an instant, he can run from the living room to the kitchen, open a cabinet, grab a box of cereal, spill it all over the floor, stomp on it, and grind it into the tile.	1.		
Most people agree that volunteers have a positive impact on our communities. But many people don't realize that volunteering can be a positive activity for the volunteer. Volunteering allows people to have meaningful new experiences. It also provides people with opportunities for leadership and the chance to develop new skills.	2.		
At different points in history, several countries have claimed Louisiana. The first inhabitants were Native Americans. In 1541, Hernando de Soto claimed the region for Spain. In the 1680s, Frenchman Sieur de La Salle named it Louisiana after King Louis XIV. During the 1700s, Britain and Spain claimed Louisiana. Then Spain gave Louisiana back to France in 1800. Finally, the United States bought Louisiana from France for $15 million.	3.		

Name _____ Date _____

> **REMEMBER** **Evidence** is information such as facts, statistics, observations, or examples that a writer uses to support a conclusion or an argument. There are different types of evidence. Logical evidence is factual. Empirical evidence is information gathered from an experiment or experience. Anecdotal evidence is based on an example or an account of an event. Also, not all evidence is equal. Reliable evidence comes from experts and is accurate, current, and plentiful. Unreliable evidence may not be detailed enough or come from a trustworthy source.

Suppose a writer makes the following claim: *Having a school dress code allows students to better concentrate on their studies.* **Read the examples of evidence that the writer has provided to support this argument. Identify each example as logical, empirical, or anecdotal. Then write whether each piece of evidence is** *reliable* **or** *unreliable.*

1. A story about several teachers disciplining students for their inappropriate clothing

   _____

2. Results of a national study that show schools with dress codes have better

   standardized test scores _____

3. A record of student test scores before and after the dress code went into effect

   _____

4. Testimony from a student who says her grades were better at her former school that

   had a dress code _____

5. Statistics that show a greater graduation rate among schools in the district with dress

   codes _____

REMEMBER A **fallacy** is an error in an argument or logic. Three types of fallacies are emotional, logical, and ethical. In persuasive writing, fallacies weaken the claim that a writer is attempting to support. Here are some common rhetorical fallacies: bandwagon appeal, appeal to pity, false dilemma (either/or), non sequitur, circular argument, hasty generalization, and personal attack (ad hominem).

Look at the following statements. Identify the fallacy each statement contains. Then explain why it is a fallacy. Use the chart in your student book to help you.

Statement	Fallacy	Explanation
My opponent is an idiot to argue against this rule.	1.	2.
Dolly has no family, so she should not have to pay the fine.	3.	4.
Everyone knows that e-mail is the best way to communicate.	5.	6.
Either we eliminate the policy or lose millions of dollars.	7.	8.
The computers are outdated because they are old.	9.	10.

GRAMMAR

Reciprocal Pronouns *Use with textbook page 234.*

> **REMEMBER** **Reciprocal pronouns** are used to show a mutual, or two-way, action or relationship. There are two main reciprocal pronouns: *each other* and *one another*. Use *each other* when talking or writing about two people, animals, or things. Use *one another* when talking or writing about more than two people, animals, or things.

Complete each sentence with the correct reciprocal pronoun.

Example: Mom and Dad help _____ with the chores.

1. The members of the club should listen to _____.

2. The two cars speeding toward _____ narrowly avoided an accident.

3. My brother and I help _____ with our homework.

4. The dogs played with _____ for hours.

5. At the party, the guests were talking to _____.

6. The foursome of golfers argued with _____ over the final scores.

7. My mother and her sister call _____ every day.

8. We propped all the posters up against _____ for support.

9. My sister and your sister resemble _____.

10. The players yelled to _____ over the noise of the crowd.

Subjunctive Mood *Use with textbook page 235.*

> **REMEMBER** Verbs in the **subjunctive mood** express conditions that do not currently exist, such as wishes and possibilities, as well as situations that are unlikely or untrue. In English, the subjunctive mood often appears as the verb *were*. However, the subjunctive mood can also be used to express demands or recommendations. In this case, the basic form of the infinitive verb should be used.

Circle the correct verb for each sentence below.

1. Would you be disappointed if I (was/were) to fail the class? _____

2. Gordon sang as if he (was/were) a trained opera singer. _____

3. The principal thought it was important that all teachers (attend/attended) the

   meeting. _____

4. She talked as though she (was/were) not involved in the accident. _____

5. Carlos's mother insists that he (cook/cooks) dinner twice a week. _____

6. He suggests that the soccer team (practice/practices) an extra hour each Monday.

   _____

7. The lawyer recommends that the defendant (tell/tells) his story truthfully.

   _____

8. James prefers that Hilda (arrive/arrives) on time. _____

WRITING

Write an Analytical Essay *Use with textbook pages 236–237.*

This is the flowchart that Stephanie used before writing her analytical essay.

Issue
1. The issue is the Graduated Driver's License (GDL) program for teenagers.

↓

Claim
2. The two-phase requirements of the GDL program are unfair to teenagers.

↓

Action
3. The GDL program should be eliminated.

↓

Thesis statement: The GDL program should be eliminated because its two-phase requirements are unfair to teenagers.

Complete your own flowchart for an analytical essay.

Issue
1.

↓

Claim
2.

↓

Action
3.

↓

Thesis statement:

Use this outline to organize your essay.

Thesis statement (claim) :
I.   Main idea:
A. Evidence:
1.   Supporting detail:
2.   Supporting detail:
3.   Supporting detail:
II.   Main idea:
A. Evidence:
1.   Supporting detail:
2.   Supporting detail:
3.   Supporting detail:
III. Main idea:
A. Evidence:
1.   Supporting detail:
2.   Supporting detail:
3.   Supporting detail:

EDIT AND PROOFREAD   *Use with textbook page 246.*

Read the paragraph carefully. Look for mistakes in spelling, punctuation, and grammar. Correct the mistakes with the editing marks on Student Book page 563. Then rewrite the paragraph correctly on the lines below.

Most students wait all year long for summer vacation There is nuthing like a summer of freedom. Most teenagers get Summer jobs, but there is still plenty of free time for fun. Teens love to spend time with their friends go to the beach and just enjoy their lives.

Even tho summer vacation offers a nice break from school work, It is a good idea to do a little academec work over the break. Reading good books is an exsellent way to strengthen your reading skills. Doing a few Math exercises each week is also a wise thing to do. It will help you remember the math you learned the previus year.

_____

_____

_____

_____

_____

_____

_____

_____

_____

_____

Underline the vocabulary items you know and can use well. Review and practice any you haven't underlined. Underline them when you know them well.

Literary Words	Key Words	Academic Words	
hyperbole	accustomed	access	affect
dialogue	entitled	community	circumstances
character motivation	offense	construction	injure
flashback	official	establishment	internal
plot	privilege	previous	predict
	protested	principle	reconstruct
	vacated	constitutional	activist
	apathy	occupying	communicate
	blog	policy	elections
	Congress	required	public
	petition	restricted	awareness
	protest	violating	publication

Put a check by the skills you can perform well. Review and practice any you haven't checked off. Check them off when you can perform them well.

Skills	I can . . .
Word Study	☐ recognize and use homophones. ☐ recognize and spell words with long *i*. ☐ recognize and use inflections -*ed* and -*ing*. ☐ recognize and spell words with long /oo/. ☐ recognize and use cognates.
Reading Strategies	☐ distinguish fact from opinion. ☐ predict. ☐ recognize sequence. ☐ evaluate new information.
Grammar	☐ use *used to* + verb and *would* + verb for habit in the past. ☐ use the simple past form of verbs. ☐ use reported speech correctly. ☐ use passive forms of modals. ☐ use reciprocal pronouns. ☐ use subjunctive mood.
Writing	☐ write an advertisement. ☐ write a critique. ☐ write a personal letter. ☐ write a letter to the editor. ☐ write an analytical essay. ☐ write a persuasive essay.

Visual Literacy: Smithsonian American
Art Museum *Use with textbook pages 248–249.*

LEARNING TO LOOK

Look at *Dollhouse* by Miriam Schapiro and Sherry Brody on page 249 of your textbook. Imagine that you could walk through that house room by room. Write five objects that you see in the house. State facts, not opinions.

Example: *I see a bear looking in a window.*

1. _____

2. _____

3. _____

4. _____

5. _____

INTERPRETATION

Look at *Dollhouse* again. Use the list of objects you observed in *Dollhouse* for the Learning to Look exercise and write five ways you think each object adds to the overall story that the artists wanted to tell.

Example: *The bear makes the house seem a little frightening.*

1. _____

2. _____

3. _____

4. _____

5. _____

Look at *Three Great Abolitionists: A. Lincoln, F. Douglass, J. Brown* by William H. Johnson on page 248 of your textbook. Pick one of the figures and create six questions you would ask him/her to learn more about his/her daily life. Use Who, Where, When, What, Why, and How to shape your questions.

Example: *My figure is the farmer.*
Example: *How many hours a day do you work?*

My figure is _____.

Who _____

Where _____

When _____

What _____

Why _____

How _____

KWLH

Look at *Dollhouse* by Miriam Schapiro and Sherry Brody on page 249 in your textbook. Answer the questions below.

K	W	L	H
What do you **know** about either one of these artists?	What do you **want** to learn about either one of these artists?	What have you **learned** about these artists?	**How** did you learn it?

UNIT 4 What does it take to beat the odds?

READING 1: "The Great Circle" / From *Touching Spirit Bear*

VOCABULARY **Literary Words** *Use with textbook page 253.*

> **REMEMBER** A **character** is a person or animal featured in a story. Writers develop character by describing how the person or animal looks and behaves. A **narrator** is the one who tells the story. In the first-person point of view, a character narrates the story. In the third-person point of view, the narrator is not a character.

Read each sentence. Underline the *characters*. Write the *point of view* (first person or third person).

1. ___*third person*___ <u>Mahmoud</u> was a tall man who sometimes wore glasses.

2. _____ She couldn't see beyond the trees and so didn't know where the forest ended.

3. _____ I found it hard to believe that Gerry had reached the mountain's summit.

4. _____ Elizabeth always ran up the stairs two at a time.

5. _____ The chipmunk ran from tree to tree, looking for more nuts.

Read the paragraph. Put a star next to the characters. From what of point of view is the story told? _____

> Ching Li examined the box she had found in the attic. It was made of tin and had gotten rusty. She could see where faded flowers had been etched in the top. She shook the box cautiously. A dull thud came from something sliding side to side. Excited, she tried to pry the box open with her fingers. That was impossible. She got a hammer from the toolbox in the basement and tried to pry the top off. Just when she was about to give up, it gave way. Before she could open it, her mother came into the room.

Read the paragraph below. Pay attention to the underlined academic words.

Mount Fuji is a well-known symbol of Japan. Many people don't realize that it's also an active volcano. The last major eruption was over three hundred years ago. The eruption damaged houses and buildings, and caused injuries, though luckily no one was killed. Although Fuji hasn't erupted for many generations, it's not smart to ignore the fact that it's an active volcano. A volcano's eruption cycle can't be easily predicted, and a major eruption could occur at any time.

Write the academic words from the paragraph above next to their correct definitions.

Example: _____*symbol*_____: picture, person, or object that represents something else

1. _____: time periods in which people of about the same age lived and died

2. _____: related events that happen again and again in the same order

3. _____: physical harm or damages caused by an accident or attack

4. _____: not pay any attention to someone or something

Use the academic words from the exercise above to complete the sentences.

5. We decided to _____ the weather reports which said that a blizzard was on the way.

6. The changing of the seasons form a _____ of weather patterns.

7. Careless bike riding causes _____ to riders.

8. Earlier _____ did not have to struggle quite as much as we do now.

Complete the sentences with your own ideas.

Example: Due to her injuries, _____*she couldn't play soccer this year*_____.

9. If you ignore traffic signs, _____.

10. One symbol of our country is _____.

WORD STUDY **Suffixes** *Use with textbook page 255.*

REMEMBER Suffixes are a group of letters added to the end of a word to form a new word. A suffix can change the meaning of a root word. The suffixes *-ness* and *-able* create words that mean having the quality of something.
Example: *well/wellness; depend/dependable*
The suffix *-ment* creates a word that describes a state.
Example: *content/contentment*
The suffix *-less* creates a word that means lacking something.
Example: *mind/mindless*

Look at the chart. Add the appropriate suffix to the word in the far left column to create a word that matches the definition in the far right column.

Root Word	-less	-ness	-able	-ment	Definition
use	*useless*				without use
1. agree					a state of agreeing with
2. kind					having a quality of being kind
3. fear					without fear
4. employ					paid work
5. enjoy					having a quality of enjoyment
6. love					without love
7. soft					having a quality of being soft

Create a new word by adding one of the following suffixes: *-less, -ness, -able, -ment*. Then add the definition next to each word. Use a dictionary, if necessary.

Example: tact ___*tactless: not showing tact*___

8. happy _____

9. commit _____

10. read _____

11. dark _____

12. manage _____

13. polite _____

14. confine _____

15. home _____

> **REMEMBER** When you read for enjoyment, you may learn new words and ideas that you will see again in nonfiction texts. You will also improve your ability to read for information.

Read the first paragraph of "The Mystery of the Hidden Cave." Pay attention to the character and setting.

The Mystery of the Hidden Cave

It was definitely a treasure map. Quentin held it carefully. It was so old that he was afraid it would fall apart in his hands. The faded ink seemed to show Monadoon Mountain, which he'd been to many times with his family. An arrow on the map pointed to the right side of the mountain, indicating an opening. Quentin had never noticed any way to get into the mountain, but maybe it was covered up with trees.

---

1. What do you think of the character and setting?

   _____

2. What do you enjoy most about the story so far?

   _____

Read the next paragraph of the story and answer the question.

Pedro was reading over Quentin's shoulder. "Look!" he pointed to a drawing of caves below the mountain. "I bet that if we can find that opening in the mountain, we can explore the caves."

Quentin nodded, his excitement rising. He wanted to go to Monadoon Mountain right now. "But how will we get there?" he wondered aloud. "We can't drive and we shouldn't let anyone else know about this."

They sat for a moment, lost in thought. As they stared at the drawing of the caves, they saw the same thing at the same time on the map. A drawing that showed a treasure chest, with what looked like gold and gems spilling out of it.

---

3. How does the author make the story fun, interesting, or exciting for you to read?

   _____

   _____

COMPREHENSION   *Use with textbook page 264.*

Choose the best answer for each item. Circle the letter of the correct answer.

1. Edwin tells Cole he needs to learn _____.

   a. pride, anger, power, and resourcefulness
   b. patience, gentleness, strength, and honesty
   c. how to fight the Spirit Bear

2. In his sleep, Cole dreamed of _____.

   a. an imaginary blanket
   b. thunder and lightning
   c. the potbellied elder

3. Cole felt frozen by fear when _____.

   a. the bear attacked
   b. the wind pummeled him
   c. lightning struck a tree

4. The shape of the moon reminded Cole of _____.

   a. the bear's head
   b. the circle of life
   c. the fallen tree

5. The next time Cole encounters a bear he will probably _____.

   a. respect it
   b. kill it
   c. run away

RESPONSE to LITERATURE   *Use with textbook page 265.*

Write a paragraph from Cole's point of view. Explain what Cole learned about the circle of life from his experience.

_____

_____

_____

_____

_____

_____

_____

Transitions and Transitional Expressions *Use with textbook page 266.*

REMEMBER To narrate events in chronological order, use transitions and transitional expressions like these: *at first, next, before, after, by the time, as, soon, then, until, when, while, in that instant,* and *finally.* Some transitions can be used to begin time clauses.

The sentences below present events in chronological order. Use transitions or the transitional expression from the box to make the order of events clear.

while	then	finally	at first	until

1. _____ he was lost.

2. _____ he found a map.

3. _____ that moment, he had been worried.

4. _____ he was walking, he began to feel better.

5. After being lost for a long time, he _____ knew where he was.

Underline the time clauses in the sentences, and circle the transitions.

Example: (Until) the rain came, the ground was dry.

6. The forest was peaceful before the blue jays landed in the tree.

7. When the birds spotted me, they made a lot of noise.

8. After the noise began to bother me, I decided to leave the area.

9. Those noisy birds followed me as I walked through the forest.

10. While I walked back to my car, the blue jays continued bothering me.

WRITING

Write a Narrative Paragraph *Use with textbook page 267.*

This is the sequence chart that Ashley completed before writing her paragraph.

At first
Brian left in a small plane to spend the summer with his father.

Then
The pilot had a heart attack. Brian landed the plane in the water.

Finally
Brian had to learn how to survive in the Canadian wilderness.

Complete your own sequence chart about a dangerous situation. It could be about you, someone you know, or someone you have read about. Arrange the events in chronological order.

At first

Then

Finally

What does it take to beat the odds?

READING 2: "Take a Chance!" / "A Survival Mini-Manual"

VOCABULARY **Key Words** *Use with textbook page 269.*

Write each word from the box next to its definition below.

| bred | equalized | expressed | maneuver | prey | stationary |

Example: _____prey_____: an animal that is hunted and eaten by another animal

1. _____: reproduced in order to develop more animals or plants

2. _____: move or turn skillfully

3. _____: made two or more things equal in size or value

4. _____: not moving; having a fixed position

5. _____: told or showed what you were feeling or thinking by using words, looks, or actions

Use the words from the box at the top of the page to complete the sentences.

6. The farmer _____ several kinds of sheep.

7. He carefully _____ their buckets of food on the scale.

8. The sheep were natural _____ for the wolves that lived in the forest nearby.

9. The farmer used dogs to _____ his flock away from the forest.

10. The sheep were usually _____ and didn't move around on very hot days.

VOCABULARY Academic Words *Use with textbook page 270.*

Read the paragraph below. Pay attention to the underlined academic words.

More people die in lightning storms than in <u>encounters</u> with sharks or bears. It is <u>estimated</u> that each year about 300 people are struck by lightning in the United States. If you are outside during a lightning storm, you should <u>definitely</u> try to get inside a building as quickly as possible. Once inside, don't touch anything that can <u>conduct</u> electricity. If there are no buildings around, get down close to the ground. Finally, if you are struck by lightning, getting to a hospital as quickly as possible can increase your chances of <u>surviving</u>.

Match each word with its definition.

Example: ___*b*___ conduct

_____ **1.** surviving

_____ **2.** definitely

_____ **3.** estimate

_____ **4.** encounter

a. judge an approximate value, amount, cost, etc.

b. allow electricity or heat to travel along or through

c. meet someone or see something without planning to

d. certainly, without any doubt

e. continuing to stay alive or exist

Use the academic words from the exercise above to complete the sentences.

5. The book shows many ways of _____ an avalanche.

6. Use math to _____ the chances that you'll roll the number 3.

7. Wood and rubber do not _____ electricity.

8. When you _____ a problem, do your best to solve it.

Complete the sentences with your own ideas.

Example: Can you estimate ___*how long the drive to Boston will take*___ ?

9. I definitely do not want to take a chance _____.

10. My first encounter with lightning was _____.

REMEMBER When *r* comes after a vowel, its sound usually changes. It often makes the sound /ûr/, which can be spelled *er* as in *nerve*, *ir* as *bird*, *or* as in *word*, and *ur* as in *burn*.

Read the words in the box below. Then write each word in the correct column in the chart.

~~butter~~ surf sir actor manor fur utter faster dirty traitor burden stir

er	ir	or	ur
butter			

Write the *r*-controlled vowel in each word below.

Example: thirty _____*ir*_____

1. her _____

2. flirt _____

3. creator _____

4. purr _____

5. father _____

6. skirt _____

7. observe _____

8. elevator _____

9. helper _____

READING STRATEGY **SKIM** *Use with textbook page 271.*

REMEMBER When you skim a text, you get a general understanding of what the text is about.

Skim the article. Skip over words you don't know. Circle the headings and illustrations. Underline topic sentences and other important ideas.

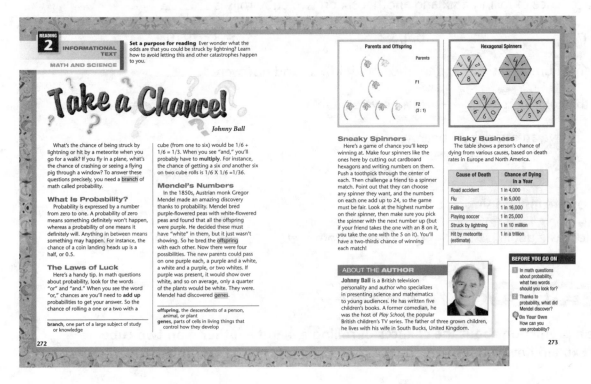

1. Circle any charts or illustrations.

2. Look at the charts and illustrations quickly. What can you learn from them about the topic of the article?

   _____

3. Are there other organizational features such as questions?

   _____

4. What is the topic sentence of the first paragraph?

   _____

5. Summarize what you learned by skimming the article.

   _____

Choose the best answer for each item. Circle the letter of the correct answer.

1. A probability of one means something _____.

   a. may happen   b. definitely will happen   c. will never happen

2. The chance of rolling a six and another six on two cube rolls is _____.

   a. 1/36   b. 1/5   c. 1/10

3. Mendel bred peas with different-colored flowers and discovered _____.

   a. the color purple   b. a new vegetable   c. genes

4. To survive an attack by a bear, you should _____.

   a. run away   b. play dead   c. climb a tree

5. If you are inside a sinking car, you should _____.

   a. lock the doors   b. stay away from metal   c. open the windows

EXTENSION *Use with textbook page 277.*

Make a prediction about the chances of rolling a 4 and another 4 on two cube rolls. Explain how you figured out the probability of that happening.

_____

_____

_____

_____

_____

_____

_____

GRAMMAR

Gerunds as Objects of Verbs and Objects of Prepositions

Use with textbook page 278.

> **REMEMBER** A gerund is a form of a verb that acts as a noun.
> **Example:** *Going* to the movies is fun.
> A gerund is formed by adding *-ing* to the base form of a verb. Gerunds can be the objects of certain verbs and the objects of prepositions.

Complete the sentences below. Use the gerund form of the verbs in parentheses.

Example: (use) Ask her about _____*using*_____ the graphics program.

1. (sneeze) This medication may help you quit _____.

2. (jog) Continue _____ around the track for ten minutes.

3. (plan) She loves _____ parties.

4. (film) Imagine _____ a scene for a movie about your life.

5. (challenge) I began the competition by _____ him to a game of chess.

Write sentences with gerunds. Follow the directions in parentheses.

Example: (Use the gerund form of *call*.)
  I only use my cell phone for calling my mom.

6. (Use the gerund form of *go*.)

   _____

7. (Use the gerund form of *say*.)

   _____

8. (Use the gerund form of *dream*.)

   _____

9. (Use the gerund form of *play*.)

   _____

10. (Use the gerund form of *avoid*.)

   _____

Write a Story with a Starter *Use with textbook page 279.*

This is the word web that Will completed before writing his paragraph.

- large building
- dark and stormy night
- field with trees
- Setting
- small shack
- lightning

Complete your own word web using a story starter based on a disaster from "A Survival Mini-Manual." List setting details in your word web.

Setting

What does it take to beat the odds?

READING 3: "John Henry" / "John Henry"

VOCABULARY **Literary Words** *Use with textbook page 281.*

REMEMBER An **archetype** is a familar type of character seen in literature throughout history. **Imagery** is used to create word pictures that appeal to the senses. **Repetition** is repeating sounds. Examples include: **alliteration** (repeated initial consonant sounds); **assonance** (repeated vowel sounds); **rhyme** (repeated ending sounds); and **rhythm** (a pattern of repeated beats or stresses).

Write each word from the box next to its definition below.

| archetype | ~~repetition~~ | alliteration | assonance | rhyme | rhythm |

Example: ___*repetition*___: repeating sounds

1. _____: a familar type of character in literature

2. _____: repeated initial consonant sounds

3. _____: repeated pattern of beats or stresses

4. _____: repeated vowel sounds

5. _____: repeated ending sounds

Read the story. Then underline the *alliteration*, circle the *rhyme*, and box the *imagery*.

The Legend of Loud Laura

Mr. and Mrs. Landers loved their tiny daughter Laura. They admired her tiny fingers and tiny toes, her tiny lips, and her super strong lungs. Mr. Landers was so happy that he burst into song: "Scream, holler, and shout. You'll never drive me out."

Little Laura's lungs were no ordinary lungs. In fact, when she hollered, drivers nearby thought they were hearing a police siren. The neighbors covered their ears.

As Laura grew older, she began singing. Today, as Loud Laura Landers, she stars in operas around the world. She is clearly heard even in the highest seats.

Read the paragraph below. Pay attention to the underlined academic words.

> Before farming machinery was invented, growing and harvesting crops was a <u>challenge</u>. Farming required a great deal of <u>physical</u> <u>labor</u>. In the late nineteenth and early twentieth centuries, new <u>technology</u>, like the invention of the tractor, made farming easier. New technology led to new farming <u>methods</u>, and people could grow more crops. During the same <u>period</u> of time, the number of railroad routes was growing quickly. Crops could be shipped more quickly and farther away.

Write the academic words from the paragraph next to their correct definitions.

Example: _____*labor*_____: work, especially work using a lot of physical effort

1. _____: relating to someone's body

2. _____: something that tests one's skill or ability

3. _____: the use of scientific or industrial methods

4. _____: length of time

5. _____: planned ways of doing something

Use the academic words from the exercise above to complete the sentences.

6. Mountain climbing takes mental and _____ strength.

7. Carrying a heavy load involves a great deal of _____.

8. Climbing Mount Everest is a _____ to even the strongest climber.

Complete the sentences with your own ideas.

Example: Modern technology _*has created better computers each year*_.

9. In the period of time I have before I go to school, I

_____.

10. The methods we use in chemistry class include _____.

WORD STUDY Spelling Long *e* *Use with textbook page 283.*

REMEMBER Long *e* can be spelled in various different ways. It can be spelled with the single letter *e* as in *be,* or with the single letter *y* as in *story.* It can also be spelled with several letter combinations such as *ea* as in *team*, *ee* as in *feet*, *ie* as in *achieve*, and *ey* as in *money.*

Circle the words in the box that contain the long *e* sound. Cross out the words that don't. Then write the words in the correct column in the chart.

(lead)　need　retrieve　red　me　my　dead　feel　eight　scary

ea	ee	e	ie	y / ey
lead				

Complete the chart with other words containing the long *e* sound and add them to the correct column. Add at least one word in each category.

ea	ee	e	ie	y / ey
each				

> **REMEMBER** To **draw conclusions**, look for clues and events in the story. Put together the clues until you can draw a conclusion.

Read the story. Then answer the questions.

License to Drive

John had just gotten his driver's license. He was thrilled. He asked his mother if he could borrow the car. She had just returned home from work and said she was too tired to drive with him. "You don't understand!" he told her. "I have my driver's license so I can drive without you." She said "Just because you have a driver's license does not mean that you can drive well. Until I consider you a good driver, you'll drive with me or another adult. Besides, we have only one car and I can't take a chance that it gets into an accident. I need that car to get to work." John nodded. His mom worked two jobs and he always tried to show her respect.

With that, John's mom went upstairs to take a nap. A little later, John's best friend, Sam, came by. "Let's go for a drive!" Sam said when he heard that John had his driver's license. "I can't," replied John. "My mom won't let me take the car."

Sam grinned, "She'll never know. She's asleep. C'mon, we'll go for a quick spin and she'll never be the wiser."

John smiled and then frowned, "But I'll be the wiser, Sam. I just can't do it."

1. From the passage, what conclusions can you draw about John's home life?

_____

2. What conclusions can you draw about Sam?

_____

3. What conclusions can you draw about John's mother?

_____

4. What conclusions can you draw about John?

_____

5. How does drawing conclusions help you to understand what you read?

_____

COMPREHENSION *Use with textbook page 290.*

Choose the best answer for each item. Circle the letter of the correct answer.

1. John Henry dreamed he was working on a _____.

   a. steamship   **b.** engine   **c.** railroad

2. The foreman didn't want to hire John Henry because he _____.

   a. didn't have a hammer   **b.** was not experienced   **c.** was from the South

3. John Henry promised to _____.

   a. race a steam drill   **b.** watch Cap'n Tommy work   **c.** stop being a steel driver

4. When the machine was ahead, John Henry _____.

   a. went to the hospital   **b.** took a break   **c.** worked with two hammers

5. The poem says that John Henry beat the steam engine by _____.

   a. six feet   **b.** four feet   **c.** fifteen feet

RESPONSE TO LITERATURE *Use with textbook page 291.*

Imagine that John Henry's story took place today. What kind of machine might he compete against? Write a new ending to his story.

_____

_____

_____

_____

_____

_____

Agreement with Generic Nouns and Indefinite Pronouns

Use with textbook page 292.

> **REMEMBER** Generic nouns, such as *a student*, *a person*, or *a man*, are used to represent a whole group. **Example:** A person has to work to get paid.
> Indefinite pronouns, such as *something*, *anyone*, and *no one*, are used in place of nouns. They don't refer to any particular person or thing. Indefinite pronouns and generic nouns must agree in person, number, and gender.

Circle the generic noun or indefinite pronoun in each sentence.

1. A man can't beat a steam engine.

2. He needs an ambulance, so could someone please get help!

3. A student needs good grades in order to graduate.

Complete each sentence by adding the correct indefinite pronoun from the box.

anyone	something	no one	everything	nothing	somebody

4. "Does _____ have a quarter I can borrow?"

5. _____ depends upon your winning the contest, so do your best.

6. _____ isn't right here. Did I leave the car door unlocked?

7. _____ knows what time the movie starts, so we should call to find out.

8. _____ told me that this restaurant has the best chocolate cake.

9. _____ needs to be cleaned here so we can come back if the house gets dirty.

10. Write your own original sentence using a generic noun or an indefinite pronoun.

   _____

WRITING

Rewrite a Familiar Story *Use with textbook page 293.*

This is the word web that Andrew completed before writing his paragraph.

Complete your own word web about "John Henry" from the point of view of Polly Ann, Li'l Willie, or the steam engine salesperson.

What does it take to beat the odds?

READING 4: From *Franklin Delano Roosevelt: The New Deal President* / From *Madam President*

VOCABULARY **Key Words** *Use with textbook page 295.*

Write each word in the box next to its definition.

advocate	championed	diagnosis	engaged	symptoms	turbulent

Example: _championed_ : supported and defended an aim or idea

1. _____: experiencing a lot of sudden change, unrest, or violence

2. _____: became involved with someone or something

3. _____: physical signs or conditions that show you may have a disease

4. _____: someone who speaks on behalf of a cause or a group

5. _____: identification of an illness

Use the words in the box at the top of the page to complete the sentences.

Example: The _____turbulent_____ events led to many disagreements.

6. The teacher was a(n) _____ for her students.

7. A high fever was one of the patient's many _____.

8. The doctor's _____ was that the patient had a bad cold.

9. The girl enjoyed the story so much that she became completely

   _____ in reading the book.

10. The students were such fans of the library that they _____ the idea of keeping it open all week.

VOCABULARY   **Academic Words** *Use with textbook page 296.*

Read the paragraph below. Pay attention to the underlined academic words.

> While vacationing with his family, Franklin Roosevelt became sick with an unknown disease. After a few weeks, instead of going away, Roosevelt's symptoms <u>intensified</u>. The third doctor the Roosevelts <u>contacted</u> told them Franklin had polio. After a while he got better, but was <u>virtually</u> unable to walk because of the disease. He <u>persisted</u> in his political career, and <u>assumed</u> the role of president during the Great Depression. He eventually became one of the most popular presidents in American history. Despite the effects of polio, Roosevelt maintained an <u>image</u> of strength during difficult times.

Match each word with its definition.

Example: __*b*__ image

_____ 1. intensified

_____ 2. assumed

_____ 3. virtually

_____ 4. contacted

_____ 5. persisted

a. increased in strength, size, or amount

b. the opinion that people have about someone or something

c. got in touch with, wrote, or telephoned someone

d. continued to exist or happen

e. took control, power, or a particular position

f. almost completely

Use the academic words from the exercise above to complete the sentences.

6. The storm _____ into a hurricane this week.

7. My homework was _____ finished by nine o'clock.

Complete the sentences below with your own ideas.

Example: My friend contacted me __*by e-mail after she moved away*__.

8. Her mother assumed a new job as _____.

9. One subject I have persisted to have trouble with is

_____.

10. The image most people have of teenagers is _____.

REMEMBER The long *o* sound can be spelled several different ways. These include *o* as in *cold*, *o_e* as in *bone*, *ow* as in *show*, and *oa* as in *roast*. Knowing these patterns helps you spell and say the words correctly.

Read the words in the box below. Then write each word in the correct column in the chart.

robot	oak	below	stove	toast	snow
pillow	loaf	soda	vote	ago	smoke

Words with long *o* spelled *o*	Words with long *o* spelled *o_e*	Words with long *o* spelled *ow*	Words with long *o* spelled *oa*
robot			

Write the letter-sound pattern in each word below.

Example: colt ___*long o spelled o*___

1. fold _____

2. drove _____

3. blow _____

4. float _____

5. own _____

6. grown _____

7. no _____

8. stone _____

9. boast _____

READING STRATEGY | SUMMARIZE | *Use with textbook page 297.*

REMEMBER To summarize is to use your own words to briefly restate the main ideas of a text. There are several steps to summarizing. First, read the text. Then reread it. Figure out the main idea in each paragraph or section. Make notes and then write a few sentences to summarize.

Read "Indira Gandhi." Then reread it and answer the questions.

> ## Indira Gandhi
>
> At the age of twelve, Indira Gandhi followed her parents' example and became involved in the future of her country, India. She marched in support of its struggle for independence from Britain. As she got older, she became more and more involved in Indian politics.
>
> In 1967, Mrs. Gandhi became the first woman elected to lead a democracy. This was an especially important achievement because India is such a large and important country. India is the world's largest democracy. That is because India has a huge population of well over a billion people.
>
> Prime Minister Gandhi led her nation through war and peace. She tried to improve the lives of the Indian people. However, she herself was a victim of violence. In 1984, she was killed by two of her bodyguards.

1. Without looking at the passage, write the main idea of the first paragraph.

   _____

2. Without looking at the passage, write the main idea of the second paragraph.

   _____

3. Without looking at the passage, write the main idea of the third paragraph.

   _____

4. Write a summary of the entire passage in one sentence.

   _____

5. How did the skill of summarizing help you to understand the passage?

   _____

Choose the best answer for each item. Circle the letter of the correct answer.

1. Dr. Lovett believed that Franklin Delano Roosevelt was suffering from _____.

   a. pneumonia   **b.** polio   **c.** malaria

2. After recovering, Roosevelt needed to use a(n) _____.

   a. wheelchair   **b.** oxygen tank   **c.** breathing tube

3. Roosevelt was elected president _____.

   a. two times   **b.** four times   **c.** three times

4. Roosevelt's New Deal programs were designed to _____.

   a. overcome physical disabilities   **b.** stop Adolf Hitler's march across Europe   **c.** aid people during the Great Depression

5. Eleanor Roosevelt changed the role of first lady by _____.

   a. championing just causes   **b.** working in Congress   **c.** living in Europe

EXTENSION *Use with textbook page 303.*

Research a president who interests you, and fill in the boxes below with information about him.

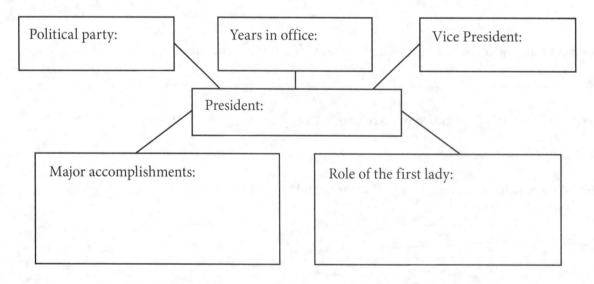

Political party:

Years in office:

Vice President:

President:

Major accomplishments:

Role of the first lady:

GRAMMAR

Habit in the Past: *Would*; Past Ability: *Could / Couldn't*
Use with textbook page 304.

> **REMEMBER** Use *would* to express what someone was in the habit of doing in the past. Use *could* or *couldn't* to express an ability or inability that someone had in the past.

Complete the sentences below with *would, wouldn't, could,* or *couldn't* + the base form of the verb in parentheses.

Example: (call) He __*would call*__ every night when he was away.

1. (think) She _____ of a reason to stay home.

2. (accept) He wanted to do it himself and _____ any help.

3. (do) She _____ the laundry because the washing machine was broken.

4. (meet) They _____ every night during the summer.

5. (speak) She _____ English before she could read it.

Answer the questions. Write sentences using *would, wouldn't, could,* or *couldn't.*

Example: What would you do when you were on vacation?
   When I was on vacation, I would go swimming every day.

6. What would you eat for a snack when you were younger?

_____

7. What sports could you play when you started high school?

_____

8. What would you do on a rainy day when you were seven?

_____

9. What is something you could draw or build or sing when you were younger?

_____

10. What is something you would collect or save when you were younger?

_____

Write a Biographical Paragraph *Use with textbook page 305.*

This is the word web that Karimah completed before writing her paragraph.

Complete your own character traits web about an individual that you consider to have beaten the odds.

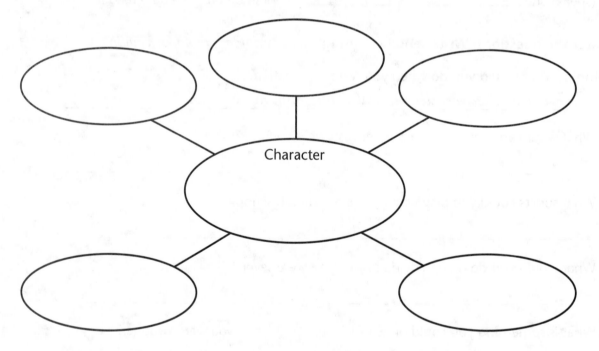

UNIT 4

What does it take to beat the odds?

READING 5: "Steve Jobs: A Virtual Genius"

VOCABULARY   **Foreign Phrases** *Use with textbook page 307.*

REMEMBER Words from other languages often become part of everyday English. This usually happens when English lacks a word with exactly the same meaning.

In the blank provided for each item in Column A below, write the letter of the correct definition in Column B.

Column A	Column B
1. _____ entente	**a.** noninterfering
2. _____ glasnost	**b.** sudden government takeover
3. _____ avant-garde	**c.** openness, freedom
4. _____ coup d'état	**d.** agreement, understanding
5. _____ laissez-faire	**e.** new, experimental

Read the sentences. Use context clues to choose the foreign word from Column A above to fill in each blank.

1. While meeting at a summit conference, the leaders of four nations reached a(n)

   _____ that would increase stability in the region.

2. During the financial boom of the late 1800s, the U.S. government adopted a(n)

   _____ policy toward industry and business.

3. After Mikhail Gorbachev endorsed a policy of _____ in the

   mid-1980s, many Soviet citizens began to speak more freely.

4. Henri Matisse was considered one of the leading artists of the French

   _____.

5. Many dictators seize power by organizing a _____ against a

   government.

Patterns and Features of Literary Nonfiction
Use with textbook pages 308–309.

> **REMEMBER** The author of a **literary biography** uses techniques of style to make a person's life story vivid and compelling. Everything in a literary biography is true, but the narrative reads more like a story or novel than an ordinary biography does.

Read the following items. Based on the author's style, decide whether each item is from a literary biography or an ordinary biography. Explain your answers.

1. "In 1946, Eleanor Roosevelt headed the United Nations Commission for Human Rights."

   _____

   _____

   _____

2. "Franklin D. Roosevelt was the only U.S. president to serve more than two terms."

   _____

   _____

   _____

3. "Eleanor championed the advancement of women and made it a point to consistently bring issues of women's equality front and center—for the president and for the nation."

   _____

   _____

   _____

4. "With his bold, innovative New Deal programs, Roosevelt made sweeping changes to bring immediate aid to those who were suffering."

   _____

   _____

   _____

LITERARY ANALYSIS

> **REMEMBER** Authors use various stylistic devices to make their writing lively and personal. Their writing usually conveys a strong **voice** that reveals their personality. These authors also use vivid **imagery**. Their **diction** and **syntax** choices also help them portray their subject in a particular way. The author's stylistic choices often reveal his or her **tone**, or attitude toward the subject.

In the personal narrative *Of Beetles and Angels*, Mawi Asgedom describes his family's experience immigrating to the United States from a Sudanese refugee camp. In the first chapter, he describes his father's perspective on the United States before they immigrated.

Read the excerpt from *Of Beetles and Angels*. Then answer the questions below.

So it was that my father started talking about a paradise called Amerikha, a distant land where everyone had a future. He told us that money grew on trees in Amerikha. Everyone was rich. Everyone had a home. Everyone had food. And everyone had peace.

Everyone lived to be one hundred years old. And had access to free education. And no wars—no wars! Yes, everyone had cars, and no one had to work more than two hours a day.

What a country! What a paradise!

1. How would you describe the author's tone? Circle your answer.

   excited   serious   angry

2. Describe Asgedom's syntax. Is it formal or casual? Explain.

   _____

   _____

3. How does Asgedom use repetition? What effect does the repetition create?

   _____

   _____

4. Why do you think Asgedom spells "America" as "Amerikha"? How does that spelling help you understand him and his family?

   _____

   _____

> **REMEMBER** The **structure** of a speech is the way it is organized and put together. Speakers organize their ideas in ways that will help make their meaning clear. The **style** of a speech is the way in which it is written. Style includes elements like diction, sentence structure and length, and tone.

Read the first paragraph from President Franklin D. Roosevelt's First Inaugural Address below. As you read, pay attention to the structure and style. Then answer the questions below.

I am certain that my fellow Americans expect that on my induction into the presidency I will address them with a candor and a decision which the present situation of our nation impels. This is preeminently the time to speak the truth, the whole truth, frankly and boldly. Nor need we shrink from honestly facing conditions in our country today. This great nation will endure as it has endured, will revive and will prosper. So, first of all, let me assert my firm belief that the only thing we have to fear is fear itself—nameless, unreasoning, unjustified terror which paralyzes needed efforts to convert retreat into advance.

1. What is the main idea of this paragraph?

   _____

   _____

2. How is the paragraph organized?

   _____

   _____

3. What is Roosevelt's tone?

   _____

   _____

4. Describe how Roosevelt's use of diction and sentence structure and length may have contributed to his overall message.

   _____

   _____

GRAMMAR

Using Negatives Correctly *Use with textbook page 316.*

> **REMEMBER** Form the negative of verbs by adding *not.* To form the simple past in the negative, use *did not* + the base verb. The word *not* is often contracted, or shortened, in informal speech and writing.

Write the negative form of these sentences.

1. It rained yesterday. _____

2. Paula loves basketball. _____

3. We will finish at 10 p.m. _____

4. Sam cleared the table. _____

5. Did you buy the tickets? _____

6. Maria switched on the light. _____

7. We designed a funny card. _____

8. I changed the flowerpots. _____

Rewrite each sentence below so that it is positive rather than negative. Make all the necessary changes in the new sentence.

1. Grandmother didn't tell an exciting story about a magician.

   _____

2. The books were not on sale, so we didn't buy them.

   _____

3. Our neighbor's children have not learned how to skateboard.

   _____

4. Sheila is not particularly interested in modern art.

   _____

5. Learning to play the drums is not a time-consuming process.

   _____

GRAMMAR

Using Contractions Correctly *Use with textbook page 317.*

REMEMBER Contractions, or shortened forms, often occur in the negative forms of auxiliary ("helping") verbs. These words include *be, have,* and *do.* Modal verbs like *can, will,* and *should* are also often contracted. The modal *will not* changes to *won't* in its contracted form.

Write the contracted forms of the verbs in these sentences.

1. I do not enjoy eating broccoli. _____

2. She had not seen the movie before. _____

3. You will not finish work early. _____

4. They did not take the plane. _____

5. The flight was not late. _____

6. Sal cannot make up his mind. _____

7. I do not like writing term papers. _____

8. We will not practice on Monday. _____

9. We do not have the tickets. _____

10. You should not speak so loudly. _____

Read the contractions below. Then write a sentence of your own using each contraction.

1. wasn't _____

2. hasn't _____

3. can't _____

4. didn't _____

5. won't _____

6. shouldn't _____

7. aren't _____

8. doesn't _____

WRITING

Write an Interpretative Response *Use with textbook pages 318–319.*

Prepare to write your interpretative response to Steve Jobs's biography by making notes below.

Main idea in the biography:

_____

_____

Major details that support the main idea:

_____

_____

I. Author's purpose in the biography:

_____

II. Author's style:

A. Choice of details: _____

_____

_____

B. Voice: _____

_____

_____

C. Tone: _____

_____

_____

D. Imagery: _____

_____

_____

III. Evaluation of the biography:

_____

_____

WRITING

Before you begin writing your interpretative response to the biography of Steve Jobs, decide what you will include in each paragraph. Remember, each paragraph needs to focus on information that supports your thesis.

Thesis statement:

_____

_____

_____

Evidence/Reasons to include in paragraph 2:

_____

_____

_____

Evidence/Reasons to include in paragraph 3:

_____

_____

_____

Evidence/Reasons to include in paragraph 4:

_____

_____

_____

Conclusion:

_____

_____

_____

EDIT AND PROOFREAD   *Use with textbook page 328.*

Read the paragraph carefully. Look for mistakes in spelling, punctuation, and grammar. Correct the mistakes with the editing marks on Student Book page 563. Then rewrite the paragraph correctly on the lines below.

I love skatebording and I am pretty good at it. Before I was ten years old I had learned the basic freestyle tricks. then I started working on aerials and some flips. When I was fourteen, disastor struck. I fell doing a complicated move and brok my left leg in three places. It took a long time to heal but I wasn't willing to give up my favorite sport. While I was still in a cast, the doctor said I can try a bit of basic skateboarding. By the time the cast came off, my weakniss had disappeared. I was almost back in top shape. And ready to polish my tricks once again. I'm really glad I didnt give up I'm competing again and loving it more than ever

_____

_____

_____

_____

_____

_____

_____

_____

_____

_____

Underline the vocabulary items you know and can use well. Review and practice any you haven't underlined. Underline them when you know them well.

Literary Words	Key Words	Academic Words	
character	bred	cycle	methods
narrator	equalized	generations	period
archetype	expressed	ignore	physical
imagery	maneuver	injuries	technology
repetition	prey	symbol	assumed
alliteration	stationary	conduct	contacted
assonance	advocate	definitely	image
rhyme	championed	encounter	intensified
rhythm	diagnosis	estimate	persisted
	engaged	surviving	virtually
	symptoms	challenge	
	turbulent	labor	

Put a check by the skills you can perform well. Review and practice any you haven't checked off. Check them off when you can perform them well.

Skills	I can . . .
Word Study	☐ recognize and use suffixes. ☐ recognize and spell *r*-controlled vowels. ☐ recognize and spell words with long *e*. ☐ recognize and spell words with long *o*. ☐ recognize and use foreign phrases.
Reading Strategies	☐ read for enjoyment. ☐ skim. ☐ draw conclusions. ☐ summarize.
Grammar	☐ use transitions and transitional expressions. ☐ use gerunds as objects of verbs and objects of prepositions. ☐ use generic nouns and indefinite pronouns. ☐ use *would* (habit in the past) and *could/couldn't* (past ability). ☐ use negatives and contractions.
Writing	☐ write a narrative paragraph. ☐ write a story with a starter. ☐ rewrite a familiar story. ☐ write a biographical paragraph. ☐ write a narrative essay. ☐ write an interpretative response.

Visual Literacy: Smithsonian American
Art Museum *Use with textbook pages 330–331.*

LEARNING TO LOOK

Look at *Lotería-Tabla Llena* by Carmen Lomas Garza on page 330 in your textbook.
Describe six things you see in this artwork. State facts, not opinions.

Example: ___*I see a wheelchair.*_____

1. _____

2. _____

3. _____

4. _____

5. _____

6. _____

INTERPRETATION

Look at *Lotería-Tabla Llena* by Carmen Lomas Garza on page 330 in your textbook.
Write a story about the scene in this artwork. Be sure to include items from the
Learning to Look exercise above.

Example: ___*The bald man in the wheelchair. . . .*_____

_____

_____

_____

_____

_____

_____

_____

_____

COMPARE & CONTRAST

Look at *Storm* by Eric Hilton on page 331 in your textbook. Use a blank piece of paper to cover the top half of *Storm*. Write three details you see in the bottom half of the sculpture.

Example: ___*There are two big bubbles.*___

_____

_____

_____

Next cover the bottom half of *Storm* and write three details you see in the upper half of the sculpture.

_____

_____

_____

How are the two halves different?

_____

_____

_____

How are the two halves similar?

_____

_____

_____

MEDIA LITERACY

Now that you have read about trying to beat the odds, go to www.Longman Keystone.com for links to the Smithsonian website. Follow the online instructions to compare the artwork in your student book with other media that convey similar messages. Which messages are conveyed more directly through visual media? Which ideas are conveyed more effectively through print or audio?

UNIT 5

How do conflicts affect us?

READING 1: From *Romeo and Juliet*

VOCABULARY   **Literary Words** *Use with textbook page 335.*

> **REMEMBER** Writers sometimes give clues about what might happen next in a story. This is called **foreshadowing**. In a play, **stage directions** tell the actors what to do while they are on stage. These instructions also explain how characters should look, what they should wear, and how they should speak.

Read the selections below that are from the script of a play. Identify each selection as an example of foreshadowing or stage directions.

Foreshadowing or Stage Directions	Selection
stage directions	[Harry's jeans and shirt are muddy.]
1.	**Harry:** Crawling under that fence didn't work. If we don't find another way into the Footes' backyard, their dog will notice us.
2.	**Jon:** Do you have a plan? I really need to get that ball back! It's my brother's. And you know how he'll react if he finds out I took it.
3.	[Jon paces back and forth nervously, while Harry stands quietly.]

Read these lines from a play. Label each example of stage directions and foreshadowing.

Scene 1

[*Uri gets up from the floor, where he has fallen. He has knocked over several chairs, and the food from his tray has splattered everywhere.*]

Uri: [*faking a smile*] OK, guys, the show's over! You can get back to your lunches!

4.

[*Uri grabs his friend Justin by the arm and pulls him aside.*]

Justin: Are you okay?

Uri: No. I can't believe this! This morning, I tripped on Leya's backpack in English class. My books went flying and now this happens. I'm going to be known as that clumsy kid in the ninth grade.

5.

Read the paragraph below. Pay attention to the underlined academic words.

I saw a play that was an <u>adaptation</u> of Mark Twain's novel *The Prince and the Pauper*. This play was a comedy, not a serious <u>drama</u>. In the play, Prince Edward and a poor boy look very similar. They decide to switch <u>identities</u> to see what it would be like. When it is time for Edward to become king, no one believes he is the prince. The court's <u>presumption</u> is that a prince would never dress like a poor boy. In the final <u>outcome</u>, Edward proves he is the real prince and becomes king.

Write the academic words from the paragraph above next to their correct definitions.

Example: _presumption_ : something that you think must be true

1. _____: a play that is serious

2. _____: final result

3. _____: the qualities that make people recognizable

4. _____: something that is changed to be used in a new or different way

Use the academic words from the exercise above to complete the sentences.

5. I don't like your _____ that I am guilty of not doing my homework!

6. The reporter kept secret the true _____ of the people he interviewed.

7. The writer was working on an _____ of the book to turn it into a movie.

Complete the sentences with your own ideas.

Example: Did you enjoy the drama that _the high school students performed_ ?

8. The last movie I saw was an adaptation of a book called

_____.

9. I thought the outcome of the movie was a surprise because

_____.

10. My presumption about your idea is that _____.

WORD STUDY Antonyms *Use with textbook page 337.*

> **REMEMBER** Antonyms are two or more words that have the opposite meaning.
> **Examples:** *easy/difficult, soft/hard.*

Look at the words in the first column of the chart. Write an antonym for each word in the second column. The first one has been done for you

Word	Antonym	Word	Antonym
cold	*hot*	**4.** always	
1. day		**5.** success	
2. ill		**6.** harsh	
3. poor		**7.** right	

Rewrite the sentences using an antonym for the underlined word.

Example: Will you have time to <u>finish</u> your homework?

   Will you have time to start your homework?

8. The play was much <u>longer</u> than expected.

  _____

9. This method of painting is very <u>easy</u> to learn.

  _____

10. Joe <u>passed</u> the examination.

  _____

11. I'm sure that the measurement is <u>correct</u>.

  _____

12. Sheila is an <u>excellent</u> student.

  _____

13. I am often <u>late</u> for my appointments.

  _____

14. She is a <u>fast</u> runner.

  _____

15. Would you <u>open</u> the window, please?

  _____

Use with textbook page 337.

> **REMEMBER** As you read, monitor your comprehension, or make sure you understand what you are reading. There are several ways to do this. You can ask yourself questions about the text. You can also stop every few paragraphs and say in your own words what you have read.

As you read the text below, ask yourself who and what it is about and where and when the events it describes take place.

In 1564, William Shakespeare was born in Stratford-upon-Avon, England. Shakespeare was the author of hundreds of poems and many plays. When he was eighteen, Shakespeare married Anne Hathaway, who was twenty-six years old. From his late twenties to his late forties, Shakespeare was an actor and writer of plays in London. He spent much of his career acting with a group known as the Chamberlain's Men.

1. Who is the text about? _____

2. Where and when do the events described in the text take place? _____

_____

3. What is the text about?

_____

As you read the next paragraph of the text, ask yourself what additional information it provides about the subject.

In the late 1500s, a horrible plague made millions of people in Europe ill. Because of this plague, theaters in London were closed for two years. During those years, Shakespeare wrote long poems, such as *Venus and Adonis*. When the theaters opened again in 1594, Shakespeare went back to writing plays.

4. What additional information about the subject does the paragraph provide?

_____

5. How can the strategy of monitoring comprehension help you to become a better reader?

_____

COMPREHENSION *Use with textbook page 346.*

Choose the best answer for each item. Circle the letter of the correct answer.

1. In this play, there is fighting between _____.

   a. Romeo and Juliet

   b. the people of Verona and the people of Florence

   c. the Capulet and Montague families

2. In one of the stage directions, a servant asks Romeo to read aloud a list of names. This list shows _____.

   a. the drinks and food that will be at a party

   b. the people who will be at a party

   c. the Capulets who will be at a party

3. Romeo goes to the party at the Capulets because _____.

   a. Benvolio convinces him to go

   b. Juliet invites him

   c. he wants to meet all the Capulets

4. The nurse tells Juliet that Romeo is a Montague. Juliet says "Monstrous love it is to me." This foreshadows _____.

   a. that Romeo and Juliet will get married and live happily ever after

   b. that it will be difficult for Romeo and Juliet to be together

   c. that the nurse wants Juliet to run away with Romeo

5. Juliet wishes that Romeo would _____.

   a. give up his fortune

   b. move away from Verona

   c. give up his name

RESPONSE TO LITERATURE *Use with textbook page 347.*

Find a scene that you like very much in the play. Draw a picture illustrating that scene. Write stage directions on the side of the picture that say how the actors are supposed to act in the scene.

Transforming Nouns into Adjectives *Use with textbook page 348.*

> **REMEMBER** Suffixes such as *-ous, -ful, -able, -y,* and *-ly* can change a noun into an adjective. For example, add the suffix *-ful* to the noun *wonder* to form the adjective *wonderful.*

Read each noun. Add the correct suffix to each noun in the chart to form an adjective. There may be several adjectives for one noun.

Noun	Adjective
hate	*hateful*
1. love	
2. villain	
3. adventure	
4. saint	
5. pain	

Complete each sentence with the correct noun or adjective in parentheses.

Example: (help/helpful) The teacher tried to be _____*helpful*_____ by using an example.

6. (grace/graceful) Most ballet dancers are extremely _____.

7. (anger/angry) Age-old _____ between the two families made communication impossible.

8. (heaven/heavenly) Angels are _____ creatures.

9. (memory/memorable) My most _____ vacation was my first trip in an RV.

10. (wonder/wondrous) Watching a child grow up is a _____ experience.

WRITING

Write a News Article *Use with textbook page 349.*

This is the graphic organizer that Kate completed before writing her news article.

Who? *Romeo, Juliet, Benvolio, and Tybalt*

Where? *Capulet ball, Verona*

When? *last night*

What? *Romeo and Juliet were talking, dancing, and kissing.*

Why? *Romeo has stolen Juliet's heart.*

Complete your own graphic organizer with the 5Ws for a gossip column about the event.

Who?

Where?

When?

What?

Why?

How do conflicts affect us?

READING 2: "Furious Feuds: Enemies by Association"

VOCABULARY   **Key Words** *Use with textbook page 351.*

Write each word in the box next to its definition.

ancestor	aristocratic	centuries	claim	descendants	rekindled

Example: ___*rekindled*___: made someone have a particular feeling or thought again

1. _____: ask for or take something that you feel belongs to you

2. _____: relating to the people in the highest social class, who traditionally have a lot of land, money, and power

3. _____: a member of your family who lived in past times

4. _____: hundreds of years

5. _____: people who are related to a person who lived long ago

Use the words in the box at the top of the page to complete the sentences.

6. I thought I wasn't mad at Jean anymore, but when I saw her, my anger was

    _____.

7. After discovering the New World, Christopher Columbus stated,

    "I _____ this land for Spain!"

8. According to our family history, we are the _____ of a king.

9. My name, Lee, is taken from the name of my _____, James Lee Murphy, who lived in the 1800s.

10. You might see very fancy furniture in the home of an _____ family.

VOCABULARY **Academic Words** *Use with textbook page 352.*

Read the paragraph below. Pay attention to the underlined academic words.

> The story "Stone Soup" takes place in a village where it hadn't rained for months and the food supplies were low. <u>Individuals</u> began hiding food from others. <u>Tension</u> worsened, and there was a great deal of <u>civil</u> unrest. A stranger came to town and said he would cook "magic" soup for the villagers. <u>Despite</u> the low food supplies, he <u>convinced</u> people to contribute ingredients for the soup. Through this, the villagers learned the importance of sharing.

Write the letter of the correct definition next to each word.

Example: ___*d*___ convinced

_____ 1. tension

_____ 2. individuals

_____ 3. civil

_____ 4. despite

a. in spite of something

b. of or pertaining to citizens (civil wars are wars between citizens of the same country)

c. the feeling that exists when people do not trust each other and may suddenly attack or start arguing

d. made someone decide to do something

e. particular people, considered separately from other people in the same group

Use the academic words from the exercise above to complete the sentences.

5. Sally says she didn't eat all the chocolate, and I am _____ that she is telling the truth.

6. In countries that are just forming, _____ wars may happen because different citizens want more power.

7. Our teacher treats all students as _____.

Complete the sentences with your own ideas.

Example: Despite the bad weather, ___*we still enjoyed the picnic*___.

8. Something that causes tension between my friend and me is

_____.

9. I think that civil rights are important because _____.

10. Despite trying hard, I sometimes _____.

Unit 5 • Reading 2

Use with textbook page 353.

> **REMEMBER** Learning common spelling patterns for long vowels will help you spell many words correctly. Each long vowel can be spelled in a variety of ways. The most common long vowel spelling patterns are the following:
>   1. A vowel surrounded by consonants and a final silent e (CVCe): *hate, ride*
>   2. A vowel team, surrounded by consonants (CVVC): *neat, week*
>   3. A syllable that ends in one or more vowels, called an open syllable (CV): *he, tea*
>   4. A consonant and vowel followed by two consonants (CVCC): *wild, mind*

Sort the words in the word box according to their long vowel spellings. Write each word in the correct column on the chart.

seed	save	dive	we	pie	host	moon	kind

CVCe	CVVC	CV & CVV	CVCC
hide	teak	me	mild

Read each of the words below to yourself. Notice the spelling pattern for the long vowel sound. Then use each word in a sentence of your own.

Example: strike (CCCVCe)   *I heard the village clock strike six.*

1. peak (CVVC) _____

2. croak (CCVVC) _____

3. tool (CVVC) _____

4. shave (CCVCe) _____

5. tie (CVV) _____

6. tame (CVCe) _____

7. child (CCVCC) _____

READING STRATEGY | **TAKE NOTES** *Use with textbook page 353.*

REMEMBER Taking notes helps you understand and remember new information. To take notes, identify your purpose for reading the text. Read quickly and make notes as you go along. Don't write complete sentences. Focus on what is important, not on the details.

Read the passage below. Take notes as you go along. Then, answer the questions.

During the 1880s, there were many violent conflicts in the American West. These feuds were often between people who owned cows and people who owned sheep. They fought over who had rights to the water in the area and where the animals could eat grass.

The Tonto Basin Feud, which began in 1882, involved two families in Arizona. The Grahams said that the Tewksburys' sheep were eating their grass. The Tewksburys would not move their sheep.

In 1887, a worker for the Tewksbury family was taking care of sheep in an area that the Grahams claimed was theirs. This worker was shot and killed by Tom Graham. This shooting made the conflict worse. Later that year, some members of the Graham family shot John Tewksbury and William Jacobs as they came out of a cabin belonging to the Tewksbury family.

After more than ten years of fighting, almost all of the members of the Graham and Tewksbury families were killed. This conflict was one of the deadliest feuds in the American West.

1. Notes. _____

_____

_____

_____

_____

2. What was your purpose for reading the text?

_____

3. Review your notes. What important ideas did you note for the first two paragraphs?

_____

4. Review your notes. What important ideas did you note for the last two paragraphs?

_____

5. How can the strategy of taking notes help you understand and remember information?

_____

Choose the best answer for each item. Circle the letter of the correct answer.

1. Yoons and Shims have been feuding for hundreds of years over _____.

   a. the graves of their ancestors
   b. the right to the throne of Korean royalty
   c. the right to display the Korean Flag

2. The best-known feud in the United States started when _____.

   a. Roseanna and Johnse met
   b. a hog wandered onto someone's property
   c. there was a conflict over where sheep could graze

3. The War of the Roses was caused by _____.

   a. a feud between the Lancaster and York families
   b. the desire for more land
   c. a love between two people from enemy families

4. From this article, you learn that feuds _____.

   a. can become violent and destructive
   b. are silly and harmless
   c. usually last only a few years

5. One important idea in this article is that _____.

   a. the feud between the Hatfields and the McCoys is the most famous feud in American history
   b. feuds always occur between families that want power over a country
   c. feuds occur all over the world and for many different reasons

EXTENSION   *Use with textbook page 359.*

What do you think creates feuds between families? Do you think feuds are caused by jealousy? Misunderstandings? Poor communication? Write down your thoughts on why the Hatfield and McCoy feud started.

_____

_____

_____

_____

_____

GRAMMAR

Showing Opposition: Adverb Clauses Beginning with
although, even though, even after

Use with textbook page 360.

> **REMEMBER** Dependent adverb clauses beginning with *although, even though,* and *even after* show opposition. Use a comma between an adverb clause and an independent clause only if the sentence begins with the adverb clause.

Connect each pair of sentences below using the subordinating conjunction in parentheses. Make sure you use correct punctuation.

Example: (although) He had been swimming for an hour. He wasn't tired.

Although he had been swimming for an hour, he wasn't tired.

1. (even though) We left early. We arrived late.

   _____

2. (although) They were good friends. Their rivalry on the tennis court was intense.

   _____

3. (even after) The actors had taken their bows. The audience applauded.

   _____

Complete each sentence using the subordinating conjunction in parentheses. Make sure you use correct punctuation.

Example: (even though) Romeo and Juliet could not get married

   even though they loved each other.

4. (although) _____
   my friend didn't come to the party.

5. (even after) _____
   the children went swimming in the lake anyway.

Write a Problem-and-Solution Paragraph *Use with textbook page 361.*

This is the problem-and-solution graphic organizer that Nola completed before writing her paragraph

Problem
Family feuds go on long after the fighting loses its meaning.

Solution
A mediator can be called in to help point out that feuds can be started or rekindled over simple things. The mediator can give examples of how such feuds have resulted in violence and death.

Complete your own graphic organizer about a clearly stated problem and solution.

Problem

Solution

How do conflicts affect us?

READING 3: From *Romiette and Julio*

VOCABULARY   **Literary Words** *Use with textbook page 363.*

REMEMBER An **allusion** in a story is a reference to a well-known person, place, event, or literary work. The **mood** of a story is the way the story makes you feel. Does the story make you feel sad? scared? happy? tense? The **plot** is the sequence of events that happen in a story. A plot usually involves characters and a main conflict.

Read each sentence. Write *mood* if it is an example of the mood of a story. Write *plot* if it is an example of the plot of a story. Write *allusion* if it is an example of an allusion.

Plot or Mood	Example
mood	The strange footsteps became louder and louder.
1.	Two teens fall in love, but then separate when one goes away to college.
2.	The two families fought like the Hatfields and McCoys.
3.	As they hid, the floor creaked. Suddenly, they heard a loud crash!

Rewrite the sentences, replacing the underlined words to create different moods.

Example: Mood happy
Sentence The *young* girl sat *happily* on the *shiny new* swings. She *smiled* as she felt the *gentle breeze* on her face.

4. **Mood** sad

   Sentence The _____ girl sat _____ on the

   _____ swings. She _____ as she felt the

   _____ on her face.

5. **Mood** tense or scary

   Sentence The _____ girl sat _____ on the

   _____ swings. She _____ as she felt the

   _____ on her face.

Read the paragraph below. Pay attention to the underlined academic words.

There was a fire in our school last winter and everyone had to go outside into the cold. Some students worried they might suffer from underline exposure if they stayed outside too long. Our fire department is made up of underline volunteers, and they put out the fire quickly. There was a rumor that our school was the underline target of an attack, but we soon learned the fire began in a chemistry lab. A student was underline identified as the starter of the fire. He had underline apparently made a mistake when blending two underline chemicals.

Write the academic words from the paragraph above next to their correct definitions.

Example: ___*chemical*___: relating to changes that happen when two substances combine

1. _____: almost certainly

2. _____: an object, person, or place chosen to be attacked

3. _____: people who offer to do something without reward or pay

4. _____: the harmful effects of staying outside for a long time in extremely cold weather

5. _____: be closely connected with an idea or group of people

Use the academic words from the exercise above to complete the sentences.

6. The dark old house on the corner has _____ been empty for a long time.

7. My school teams can be _____ by their red and yellow uniforms.

8. Police guarded the airport, which they thought might be the _____ of an attack.

Complete the sentences with your own ideas.

Example: The chemical reaction in the lab caused an ___*explosion*___.

9. To avoid exposure, in the winter I wear _____.

10. I think that volunteers _____.

WORD STUDY Prefixes *in-*, *im-*, *inter-*, *re-*, and *un-*

Use with textbook page 365.

> **REMEMBER** A prefix is a letter or group of letters that can be added to the beginning of a word to change its meaning. Learning the meaning of common prefixes will help you figure out the meanings of many words you read and hear. The prefixes *in-*, *im-*, and *un-* can mean "not." The prefix *inter-* means "between," and the prefix *re-* means "again."

Use what you have learned about prefixes to figure out the meanings of the new words on the chart. Then write the meaning of each word on the chart.

Prefix	Base Word	New Word
in- +	correct	incorrect *"not correct"*
im- +	precise	imprecise **1.**
inter- +	state	interstate **2.**
re- +	build	rebuild **3.**
un- +	afraid	unafraid **4.**

Use what you have learned about prefixes to define the words below. Write the meanings of the words. Then use each word in a sentence of your own.

Example: (inaudible) _not audible; He spoke so quietly; his voice was inaudible._

5. (indescribable)_____

6. (incapable)_____

7. (impatient)_____

8. (interact)_____

9. (reinvest)_____

10. (reassure)_____

11. (unappreciated)_____

12. (unavailable)_____

REMEMBER Sometimes a writer doesn't tell you everything in a story. You have to figure things out yourself. When you use clues from a story as well as what you already know to figure something out, you make inferences.

Read each passage. Choose a logical inference you can make, based on the information in the passage and what you already know.

1. Susanna jumped up. Her blanket tumbled to the floor as she rubbed her eyes. "Where was that ringing sound coming from?" she wondered.

   a. Susanna is in school.   **c.** Susanna shares a room with her sister.
   b. Susanna is in bed.

2. Jordan sat in his new room, surrounded by boxes. He didn't want to unpack them; he just wanted to go back to his old home.

   a. Jordan likes boxes.   **c.** Jordan has moved to a new home.
   b. Jordan likes his new room.

Read each passage. Answer each question by making an inference based on the text and your own knowledge.

3. "Stop opening and closing your window!" shouted Mom from the front seat.
   "But I'm so bored. When will we get to Uncle Ray's?" whined Elana.

   Where are Elana and her mother?

   _____

   _____

4. Lai noticed a six-year-old boy who was crying. Lai asked, "Are you okay?" The boy looked up at Lai, "I can't find my big brother," he said. Lai squeezed his hand. "I'll help you find him. Don't worry."

   From the passage, what can you infer about Lai's personality?

   _____

   _____

5. How can the strategy of making inferences make you a better reader?

   _____

COMPREHENSION *Use with textbook page 372.*

Choose the best answer for each item. Circle the letter of the correct answer.

1. The Devildogs don't like that Romiette _____.

   a. doesn't want to join their gang

   b. isn't friends with Malaka anymore

   c. is dating Julio, who isn't black

2. Malaka tells Romiette that _____.

   a. the Devildogs want to make a statement

   b. Terrell will protect both of them

   c. Romiette should have dated someone Mexican instead

3. Romiette is afraid to jump out of the boat because _____.

   a. she is terrified of water

   b. she doesn't think the Devildogs will protect her

   c. the water is too cold

4. Julio finds Romiette in the water and _____.

   a. then loses her again

   b. drags her to safety

   c. flags down a passing boat

5. In the last section of this story, you learn that _____.

   a. Malaka really loved Julio and wanted to save Romiette

   b. the Cappelles and Montagues become friends

   c. Julio joined the Devildogs and left Romiette

RESPONSE to LITERATURE *Use with textbook page 373.*

Think about the relationship between Romiette and Julio. Do you think they should have told their parents about the situation? Why or why not?

_____

_____

_____

_____

_____

Modals of Advisability: *should, ought to, had better;*
Adverb Clauses of Condition: *if*

Use with textbook page 374.

REMEMBER Use *should* and *ought to* to give advice about something a person should do.
Example: You should look both ways before crossing the street.
Use *should not* or *ought not* to advise a person not to do something.
Example: You should not abandon a friend in need.
Use *had better, had better not,* and *if* clauses to give warnings.
Example: You had better not go swimming in the deep end of the lake.

Rewrite each sentence to give advice, using the word or words in parentheses.

Example: (should not) Don't try to handle a crisis alone.

You should not try to handle a crisis alone.

1. (should not) Don't go there alone at night.

   _____

2. (ought to) Listen to me.

   _____

3. (had better) When driving, you need to obey all traffic rules.

   _____

4. (had better not) We need to make sure that we do not arrive late.

   _____

5. (if) The doctor does not act fast. The patient may suffer.

   _____

WRITING

Support a Position *Use with textbook page 375.*

This is the word web that Karimah completed before writing her paragraph.

```
        Position
Schools should take steps
   to discourage gangs.

   Support                    Support
Student policies say groups   Gangs can lead to
  must be open to all.         major violence.

            Support
      People in gangs have no
      voice and must follow
          gang rules.
```

Complete your own word web about a position that you support.

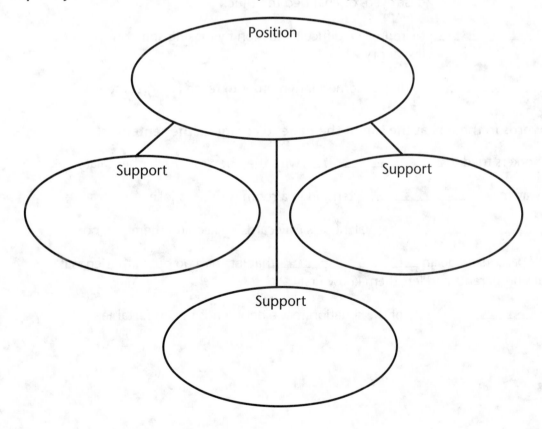

```
            Position



  Support              Support




        Support
```

How do conflicts affect us?

READING 4: From *Conflict Resolution: The Win-Win Situation*

VOCABULARY **Key Words** *Use with textbook page 377.*

Write each word in the box next to its definition.

| accommodation | avoidance | compromise | defuse | negotiate | preserves |

Example: *accommodation* : a way of solving a problem between two people or groups so that both are satisfied

1. _____: to end an argument by making an agreement in which everyone involved accepts less than what he or she wanted at first

2. _____: deliberately staying away from someone or something

3. _____: keeps something or someone from being harmed, destroyed, or changed too much

4. _____: to improve a difficult situation by making someone less angry

5. _____: to discuss something in order to reach an agreement

Use the words in the box at the top of the page to complete the sentences.

6. The workers tried to _____ with their bosses for a higher salary.

7. One way to _____ tension in a room is to tell a joke.

8. Rose _____ her Valentine's Day cards by keeping them in a box.

9. Ricky's parents made an _____ that lets him go out with friends if he calls his parents and lets them know first.

10. Her _____ of the situation made her friends uncomfortable.

VOCABULARY Academic Words *Use with textbook page 378.*

Read the paragraph below. Pay attention to the underlined academic words.

Even close friends have arguments once in a while. No matter what issues cause the disagreement, it's important to be principled. Focus on explaining and clarifying both points of view. Be sure to validate each other's feelings even if you don't agree on everything. Most disagreements can be easily cleared up in this way.

Write the letter of the correct definition next to each word.

Example: __*b*__ clarifying

      a. subjects or problems that people discuss or debate

_____ **1.** validate

      b. making something easier to understand by explaining it in more detail

_____ **2.** issues

      c. having strong beliefs about what is right and wrong

_____ **3.** principled

      d. recognize or acknowledge

Use the academic words from the exercise above to complete the sentences.

4. My teacher feels that it's important to _____ good work.

5. The _____ in the presidential debate took a long time to discuss.

6. Terry is a very _____ person; she always tries to do the right thing.

7. I need help _____ my plan.

Complete the sentences with your own ideas.

Example: By clarifying the idea, the teacher can help the students
   understand what she means.

8. One of the issues that affects my community is _____.

9. I think it's important to be principled because _____.

10. I validate my friends' ideas by _____.

Use with textbook page 379.

> **REMEMBER** The long and short *u* sounds can both be spelled with the letter *u*. The long *u* sound is also commonly spelled *ew* as in *few*, *ue* as in *argue*, *ou* as in *you*, and *u_e* as in *huge*. The short *u* sound is most often spelled *u*, but it can also be spelled *ou* as in *trouble*.

Look at the words in the word box below. Say each word to yourself and identify the vowel sound. Sort the words according to the long or short *u* sound. Write the words in the correct column in the chart below. Then circle the letter or letters that stand for the long and short *u* sounds.

~~unit~~	ton	music	plum	fuel	
refuge	from	double	cue	few	trunk

Long vowel /ū/	Short vowel /u/
unit	

Write two words that contain a long *u* sound and two words that contain a short *u* sound. The words you write should not appear in the word box on this page. Then use each word in a sentence of your own.

Words with a short *u* sound:

1. _____

2. _____

Words with a long *u* sound:

3. _____

4. _____

READING STRATEGY | COMPARE AND CONTRAST

Use with textbook page 379.

REMEMBER When you compare, you tell how two or more things are alike. When you contrast, you tell how two or more things are different. A Venn diagram can help you organize your thoughts.

Read each passage. Then answer the questions.

Migraine headaches are caused by a change in the size of arteries, or blood vessels, in the head. Cluster headaches are also caused by changes in the size of arteries. For both types of headaches, the change in artery size causes pressure and pain in the head.

1. **How are migraine headaches and cluster headaches the same?**

   _____

Migraine headaches last from four hours to a week, but cluster headaches usually last about thirty to forty-five minutes. About one-third of people who have migraine headaches feel an "aura," or a feeling that they will get a migraine, before the pain begins. Unlike migraines, cluster headaches come with no warning.

2. **How are migraine headaches and cluster headaches different?**

   _____

Feeling stressed or tired can bring on a migraine. Some foods and drinks, such as chocolate and alcohol, can also cause a migraine. It is not as well known, however, what causes cluster headaches. Scientists think that, as with migraines, alcohol can cause cluster headaches.

3. **Explain one way in which a migraine headache and a cluster headache are the same and one way in which they are different.**

   _____

4. Use a Venn Diagram to compare and contrast migraines and cluster headaches.

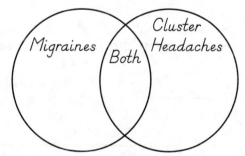

5. **How can the strategy of comparing and contrasting help you better understand a text?**

   _____

Choose the best answer for each item. Circle the letter of the correct answer.

1. When you are arguing with someone, it is a good idea to _____.

   a. try to see the other person's point of view
   b. leave the situation unresolved
   c. yell as loud as you can until the other person leaves

2. Active listening means _____.

   a. ignoring the person who is speaking
   b. hearing and understanding the person who is speaking
   c. talking while someone else is speaking and interrupting them

3. When you are listening to someone who is arguing with you, you should use a

   technique such as _____.

   a. avoiding
   b. ignoring
   c. clarifying

4. One similarity between soft conflict and hard conflict resolution responses is that

   _____.

   a. both responses work well in all situations
   b. both responses bring about one-sided losses or gains
   c. both responses result in more fights

5. The author believes that one way to save a relationship is to solve problems with a

   _____.

   a. principled response
   b. friendly response
   c. hard response

EXTENSION   *Use with textbook page 385.*

Think about the three types of responses to conflict. Read the statement below. Write how you might respond to the statement with each type of response.

Statement	Response
Your friend says, "I lost your favorite CD, and I don't have enough money to buy a new one."	(hard) *Get me a new one now! I don't care if you don't have enough money!*
	(soft)
	(principled)

GRAMMAR

Present Real Conditional *Use with textbook page 386.*

> **REMEMBER** The present real conditional expresses true, factual ideas. The *if* clause indicates the condition and the result clause indicates what happens if the condition is met. Use the simple present in both clauses. If you aren't certain of the result, you can use a modal such as *can, might,* or *must* in the result clause.
> **Example:** I think I can boost my grades If I do this extra project.
> Use a comma between the *if clause* and main clause only if the sentence begins with the *if* clause.
> **Example:** If I wear a helmet when biking, I have a better chance of not getting injured.

Combine each pair of sentences using the present real conditional. Make sure to use the correct punctuation.

Example: You are tired. You are grumpier than usual.

If you are tired, you are grumpier than usual.

1. Work out regularly. You might become stronger.

_____

2. Read the paper every day. You learn a lot about current affairs.

_____

3. Practice the piano. You may become a pianist.

_____

Write an answer to each question below using the present real conditional. Make sure to use correct punctuation.

Example: You go to bed too late. What happens?

If you go to bed too late, you are tired.

4. It rains. What happens?

_____

5. You watch a lot of TV. What happens?

_____

Write to Compare and Contrast *Use with textbook page 387.*

This is the three-column chart that Chelsea completed before writing her paragraph.

Soft response	Hard response	Principled response
tries to avoid Katherine, pretend everything is OK		*take Katherine aside and talk about it*
tension builds, is annoyed, could take out stress on others	*feels bad and accomplishes nothing*	*can get the results she needs and preserve her relationship*

Complete your own three-column chart about a conflict that can be resolved using a principled response.

Soft response	Hard response	Principled response

How do conflicts affect us?

READING 5: "Hometown Hero"

VOCABULARY **Root Words in Content-Area Classes**
Use with textbook page 389.

REMEMBER Many English words used in your content-area classes come from Latin and Greek roots. If you know what the root of a word means, you can more easily figure out the meaning of the whole word.

Try to figure out the meaning of the underlined word in each sentence below. Use both your knowledge of Greek and Latin roots and any context clues. Write your best guess on the first line. Then look up the word in a dictionary and write the dictionary definition on the second line. See if you were correct.

1. The U. S. <u>Centennial</u> of Flight Commission was founded in 2003 to celebrate the Wright Brothers' first flight, which took place in 1903.

   _____

   _____

2. The first <u>transcontinental</u> railroad in the United States was completed in 1869 and connected the east and west coasts by rail for the first time.

   _____

   _____

3. U. S. companies <u>import</u> many products from other countries to sell in the United States.

   _____

   _____

4. Detectives may bring in a <u>graphologist</u> to analyze a handwritten letter for clues to its author's identity.

   _____

   _____

REMEMBER Asking for something politely requires special words. *Saying please* and *thank you* are important, but word choice is important, too. To most native speakers of English, *would* and *could* sound more polite than *will* and *can*. There are also phrases that sound polite to English speakers.

Read these requests. Decide whether each one is a polite way to ask for something. Then rewrite the impolite ones in the box below.

1. Could you please hand me the tortillas?

2. Give me the potato salad.

3. Would you mind opening that door for me?

4. Would it be possible for me to watch the rehearsal?

5. I want the hammer.

6. Could I ask you to carry this box for me?

7. Can I have that book?

Name _____ Date _____

Use with textbook page 391.

REMEMBER People often signal their understanding of what you are saying without speaking. They may nod or frown to signal whether they understand. It is important to look for these **nonverbal cues**. It is also important to try different methods of communicating. If you do not remember a particular word, you can **say it another way**, for example you can use a synonym—a word that means almost the same thing. You can also describe the thing or explain the idea you are trying to communicate. You can use gestures or even act out the word you cannot remember.

Look at each description in the left column. See if you can figure out the word that is being described. Write it in the box at the right.

Description	Word
It comes from trees and people build things with it, such as chairs and tables.	
It is clear and you drink it. You can also swim in it. It falls from the sky when it rains.	
It is red on the outside and about the size of an orange. It grows on a tree. It is white on the inside and crisp.	
It is where you hang your clothes. It has a door.	
It is what you type on to send e-mails and surf the Internet.	
It is something you write with.	

Now, write a description in the left column for each word in the right column.

Description	Word
	cup
	tomato
	street
	store
	shoes
	kitchen
	map

LITERARY ANALYSIS Structure and Elements of Drama
Use with textbook pages 392–393.

> **REMEMBER** An **archetype** is an original model or pattern from which other things of the same type are copied. An archetype can be a type of character, image, or situation that appears in literature from around the world and throughout history.

Read the following passage. Then decide which archetype each character represents. On the lines, explain why each character fits that archetype.

> "Gee, I've never seen so many tall buildings," Sue said. She'd just arrived in the city, after leaving her small hometown for the first time. The buildings made her feel smaller and less powerful than she had ever felt in her life.
>
> "They're just brick and steel," said her cousin Maria. She thought Sue's fresh way of looking at things was funny.
>
> "Very big brick and steel," said Sue. She stepped back to get a better look at a skyscraper. As she stepped back, her foot slipped off the curb. In an instant, she had fallen into the street, in the way of oncoming traffic.
>
> Maria jumped off the curb after Sue, grabbed her, and pulled her back to safety. A taxicab driver whooshed by in his cab, honking his horn.
>
> "You saved my life!" said Sue.
>
> "But not your pants," said Maria. They both looked at the tear in Sue's new white jeans and laughed.

Hero	Outsider	Innocent Person	Wise Person

Sue Archetype: _____

_____

_____

_____

Maria Archetype: _____

_____

_____

_____

> **REMEMBER** A **motif** is an idea or image that is repeated in a play, story, or poem. The purpose of a motif is to help develop an important idea. A motif can be a recurring idea, such as the difference between truth and lies or appearances and reality. However, it can also be a recurring image.

Read the following passage. Then identify the motif that is repeated. In the table below, write what the motif is and what idea it helps to develop.

Spring was here and everything was new! Sweet and tender shoots of grass poked up through the dirt. Crocuses opened every morning, in fresh whites and yellows. Everywhere you looked there were new beginnings.

It was spring in Nita's heart, too. The last few months had been very difficult. Her sister Lisette had been sick, and the family had worried. Nita's father was told he might lose his job. And Nita's best friend had moved away.

But now, Lisette was healthy again. Nita's father lost his job, but he had a new, better one. And Nita had just received a letter from her friend.

Nita also had a new friend, someone she could really talk to. The loneliness of winter was gone, and a new happiness was growing in her heart like spring flowers.

Motif	Idea that the motif develops

Name _____ Date _____

> **REMEMBER** A **script** for a play should have a theme, or main idea. Themes can be implicit (unstated) or explicit (stated). A script should also have a particular mood and tone. A writer creates mood through his or her description of the characters, settings, and objects. The tone is the writer's attitude toward his or her subject.

Use this chart to help generate ideas for your script. Write your ideas on the lines.

Who are the characters?

_____

_____

_____

What is the situation, and what happens to the characters?

_____

_____

_____

How do they feel about what happens to them? (What is the mood?)

_____

_____

_____

What is my attitude toward the characters and their situation? (What is the tone?)

_____

_____

_____

What lesson does the audience learn? (What is the theme? Is it implicit or explicit?)

_____

_____

_____

_____

Write what will happen in each scene of your script in the flowchart below.

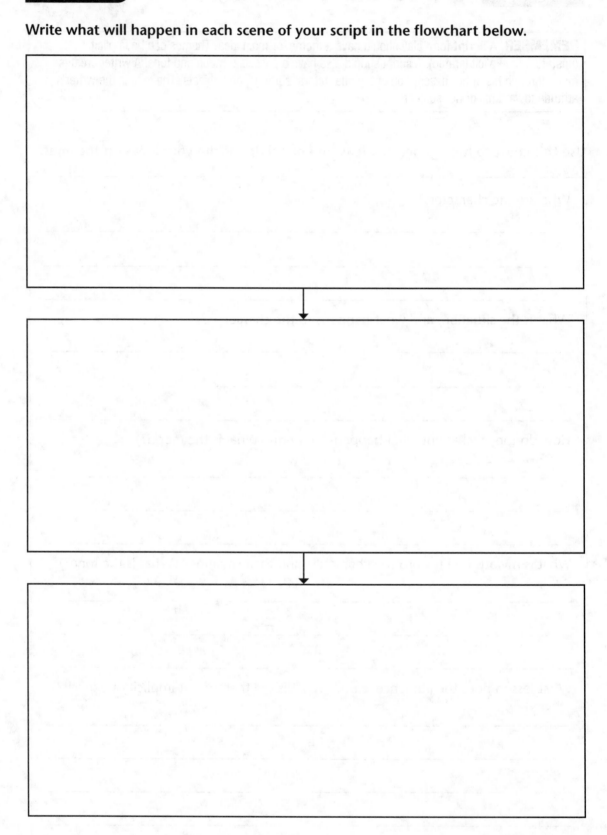

EDIT AND PROOFREAD   *Use with textbook pages 410.*

Read the paragraph below carefully. Look for mistakes in spelling, punctuation, and grammar. Correct the mistakes with the editing marks on Student Book page 563. Then rewrite the paragraph correctly on the lines below.

> I knew I shouldn't of gone to the party without telling my best Friend, Marie. I was worried that she would be upset if I told her becaues she wasn't allowed to go. Of course, she found out that I went. Cheryl telled her. Now she's really angry at me and doesn't think I'm a good freind. I really like Marie, and I didn't mean to hurt her Feelings. I ought to have be honest with her. I had better tried to be a more sensitive friend in the future I feel terrible about this. I hope Marie will forgive me.

_____

_____

_____

_____

_____

_____

_____

_____

_____

_____

Underline the vocabulary items you know and can use well. Review and practice any you haven't underlined. Underline them when you know them well.

Literary Words	Key Words		Academic Words	
foreshadowing stage directions allusion mood plot	ancestor aristocratic centuries claim descendants rekindled	accommodation avoidance compromise defuse negotiate preserves	adaptation drama identities outcome presumption civil convinced despite individuals tension	apparently chemical exposure identified target volunteers clarifying issues principled validate

Put a check by the skills you can perform well. Review and practice any you haven't checked off. Check them off when you can perform them well.

Skills	I can . . .
Word Study	☐ recognize and use antonyms. ☐ recognize and use long vowel spelling patterns. ☐ recognize and use words with prefixes *in-, im-, inter-, re-,* and *un-*. ☐ recognize and spell words with long and short *u*. ☐ recognize and use root words.
Reading Strategies	☐ monitor comprehension. ☐ take notes. ☐ make inferences. ☐ compare and contrast.
Grammar	☐ transform nouns into adjectives. ☐ use adverb clauses beginning with *although, even though, even after*. ☐ use modals of advisability: *should, ought to, had better*, and adverb clauses of condition: *if*. ☐ use present real conditionals.
Writing	☐ write a news article. ☐ write a problem-and-solution paragraph. ☐ write a paragraph to support a position. ☐ write a compare-and-contrast paragraph. ☐ write an expository essay. ☐ write a script.

Visual Literacy: Smithsonian American
Art Museum *Use with textbook pages 412–413.*

LEARNING TO LOOK

Look at *Comanche Warriors, with White Flag, Receiving the Dragoons* by George Catlin on page 412 in your textbook. Write five objects that you see. State facts, not opinions.

Example: ___white flags_____

1. _____

2. _____

3. _____

4. _____

5. _____

INTERPRETATION

Look at *Comanche Warriors, with White Flag, Receiving the Dragoons* again. What do you think is happening in the painting? Write down your ideas. Make sure that your interpretation can be explained by the details you observed for the "Learning to Look" exercise.

Example: ___Men are carrying white flags for a reason._____

_____

_____

_____

_____

_____

_____

_____

Look at *Comanche Warriors, with White Flag, Receiving the Dragoons* again and *State Names* by Jaune Quick-To-See Smith on page 413 in your textbook to complete the diagram below. Describe each piece of art in the outside sections of the diagram. Then list the similarities between the two paintings in the center where the two circles overlap.

George Catlin
Comanche Warriors, with White Flag, Receiving the Dragoons

Similarities

Jaune Quick-To-See Smith
State Names

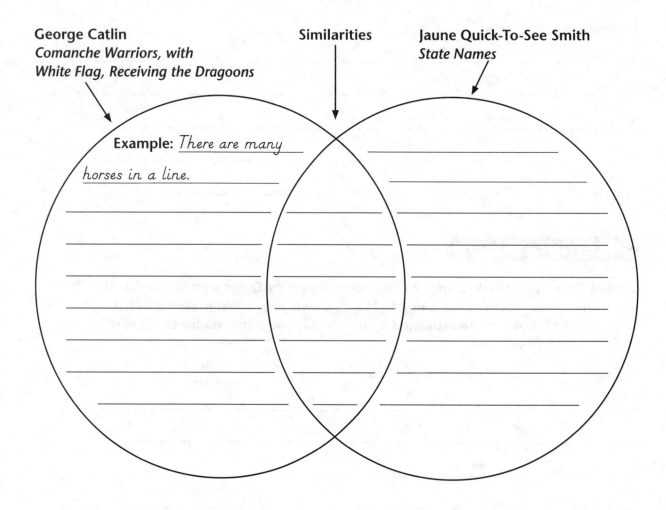

Example: *There are many horses in a line.*

UNIT 6

Do things really change?

READING 1: From *Catherine, Called Birdy* / "The Dinner Party"

VOCABULARY **Literary Words** *Use with textbook page 417.*

> **REMEMBER** In stories that use the **first-person point of view**, events are told from a character's perspective. This point of view uses words like *I, me,* and *my*. In stories that use the **third-person point of view**, events are told through the eyes of someone other than a character. The third-person point of view uses words like *he, she, him, his,* and *her*.

Read each sentence. Write *first* if it uses first-person point of view or *third* if it uses the third-person point of view.

First-person or third-person point of view?	Sentence
third	He decided to call her.
1.	My alarm clock didn't go off, so I was late.
2.	Julie was glad that she remembered her umbrella.
3.	I drove to my grandmother's house.

Read the passages below. Circle the five words in each passage that tell you whether it is written in the first-person or third-person. One of the five words is circled for you as an example. Then at the end, circle *First-person* or *Third-person*, depending on whether the passage is told from the first-person or third-person point of view.

4. (I)went to the floating swimming pool today. I'm not kidding. It's a pool that floats on a barge in the river. As I floated on my back in the cool water, I could see the city skyline.

   First-person   Third-person

5. (She)decided to go to the new floating swimming pool. She had to wait in a long line to get in. Finally, it was her turn. She floated on her back in the cool water and looked up at the city skyline.

   First-person   Third-person

Read the paragraph below. Pay attention to the underlined academic words.

> Until recently, the <u>tradition</u> in many cultures was that parents chose their child's marriage partner. Marriage partners were decided according to <u>economics</u>, not love. Parents chose a marriage partner of good economic <u>status</u>. Typically, parents would not have <u>consented</u> to a marriage based on love alone. Thankfully, in modern times there has been a <u>reaction</u> against this type of marriage. Most people around the world now marry for love.

Write the academic words from the paragraph above next to their correct definitions.

Example: ___*reaction*___ : something you feel or do because of what has happened or been said to you

1. _____ : something that people have done for a long time and continue to do

2. _____ : relating to the development and management of wealth

3. _____ : your social or professional rank or position in relation to other people

4. _____ : agreed

Use the academic words from the exercise above to complete the sentences.

5. The _____ to the plague in Europe was great fear.

6. My mother _____ to let me drive her car.

7. Celebrities and athletes have a lot of _____ in American culture.

Complete the sentences with your own ideas.

Example: Our teacher consented to giving us less homework because

___*of the holiday weekend*___ .

8. My family has a tradition of _____ .

9. In economics class, we learned about _____ .

10. When my friend told me she won the

contest, my reaction was _____ .

WORD STUDY **Silent Letters** *Use with textbook page 419.*

> **REMEMBER** The letters, *wr, kn, gn,* and *mb* stand for one sound when they appear at the beginning or end of a word or syllable. For example: the *w* is silent in *wrong*, the *k* is silent in *knife*, the *g* is silent in *gnat*, and the *b* is silent in *numb*. Learning these patterns helps you say and spell the words correctly.

Read the words in the box below. Then write each word in the correct column in the chart.

| wrote | design | knack | crumb | wretch | gnaw |
| plumber | wrist | gnarled | thumb | knob | knowledge |

Words with wr	Words with kn	Words with gn	Words with mb
wrote			

Write the silent letter-sound pattern in each word below.

Example: dumb ___*mb; silent b*___

1. gnome _____

2. wrestle _____

3. knock _____

4. tomb _____

5. wreck _____

6. knit _____

7 bomb _____

8. wreath _____

9. align _____

REMEMBER As you read, it is important to check your understanding of the text you are reading. One good technique is to ask questions using the 5Ws: *who, where, when, what,* and *why.*

As you read the paragraph below, ask yourself questions using the 5Ws. Then answer the questions that follow.

The windows were open, but the room was hot and still. It was hard to hear the principal over the sound of the ladies fanning themselves. Bella's brother Jeremy squirmed. "Can I take off my jacket?" he whispered. Bella gave him a look. He stopped but soon started fidgeting again. Bella couldn't blame him, but he had to learn how to behave properly. This was their big sister's graduation, after all.

1. Who are the main characters in the text?

   _____

   _____

2. What is the relationship between the two characters in the text?

   _____

   _____

3. What clues in the text tell you where the story takes place?

   _____

   _____

4. What clues in the text reveal why Bella treats her brother the way she does?

   _____

   _____

5. How do you think asking questions can help you to read with better comprehension?

   _____

   _____

COMPREHENSION   *Use with textbook page 426.*

Choose the best answer for each item. Circle the letter of the correct answer.

1. Catherine realizes that her father is asking her questions because he wants to _____.

   a. send her to learn a trade   **b.** marry her off   **c.** send her to school

2. Catherine does not want _____.

   a. to be a rich lady   **b.** to read and write   **c.** to be married

3. When she meets her suitor, Catherine decides to _____.

   a. spoil her father's plans   **b.** marry him right away   **c.** go to her room and read Latin

4. In "The Dinner Party," the hostess _____.

   a. tries to quietly draw a cobra out from under the table   **b.** shouts at the colonel because of his prejudice against women   **c.** talks to the silent American scientist

5. The narrator of the story shows that the colonel is _____.

   a. just   **b.** wrong   **c.** right

RESPONSE TO LITERATURE   *Use with textbook page 427.*

Imagine what will happen when the novel *Catherine, Called Birdy* continues. What do you think will happen when the next suitor arrives?

_____

_____

_____

_____

_____

Adjective Clauses: Relative Pronouns as Subjects and Objects

Use with textbook page 428.

REMEMBER An adjective clause begins with a relative pronoun and describes a noun in the main clause. The relative pronoun *who* describes people. Use it as the subject of a clause. The relative pronoun *whom* also describes people. Use it only as the object of a clause. The relative pronoun *that* can be used to describe people or things. Use it as the subject or object of a clause.

Circle the correct relative pronoun in each sentence.

Example: We read the book ((that)/ whom) she wrote.

1. The player (who / whom) won the tournament celebrated his victory.

2. The movie (that / whom) we watched last night was funny.

3. She is a woman (who / whom) I admire.

4. The book (that / whom) she recommended is about the Middle Ages.

5. The students (that / whom) prepare their assignments succeed in their classes.

Complete each sentence with the correct relative pronoun.

Example: The letter _____*that*_____ she received contained bad news.

6. Stories _____ are funny make people laugh.

7. I admire people _____ have the courage to tell the truth.

8. The children _____ I saw seemed very happy.

9. The house _____ my father built has a beautiful garden.

10. The people _____ we met at the party were charming.

WRITING

Write an Introductory Paragraph *Use with textbook page 429.*

This is the word web that Michael completed before writing his paragraph.

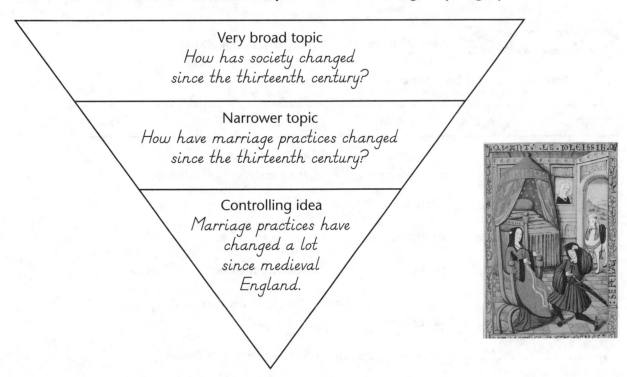

Very broad topic
How has society changed since the thirteenth century?

Narrower topic
How have marriage practices changed since the thirteenth century?

Controlling idea
Marriage practices have changed a lot since medieval England.

Complete your own inverted pyramid graphic organizer to help you narrow a question.

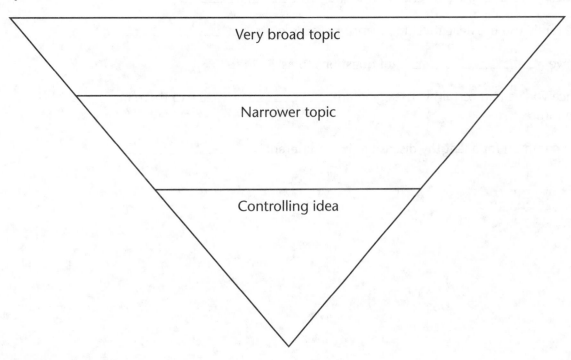

Very broad topic

Narrower topic

Controlling idea

Do things really change?

READING 2: From *Oh Rats!: The Story of Rats and People* /
From *Outbreak: Plagues That Changed History*

VOCABULARY   **Key Words** *Use with textbook page 431.*

Write each word in the box next to its definition.

epidemic	fragility	host	immune	society	stages

Example: ___*epidemic*___ : a large number of cases of an infectious disease

1. _____: a large number of

2. _____: weakness

3. _____: particular points or times in a process

4. _____: all people who live in the same country and share the
   same laws

5. _____: not able to be affected by a disease or illness

Use the words in the box at the top of the page to complete the sentences.

6. Officials are trying to prevent an avian flu _____.

7. We rarely use the delicate china teapot because of its _____.

8. I have a _____ of questions to ask.

9. Once you've had certain viruses, you are _____ to them in
   the future.

10. It is common for a lengthy disease to have different _____.

VOCABULARY **Academic Words** *Use with textbook page 432.*

Read the paragraph below. Pay attention to the underlined academic words.

Malaria is a deadly disease. It is especially common in hot, humid <u>regions</u>. This is because mosquitoes are the <u>predominant</u> carriers of the disease. Scientists would like to <u>eliminate</u> malaria in the poorer countries where it still exists. Mosquito nets are used to prevent the spread of the disease; not using the nets will <u>expose</u> people to the mosquitoes that carry malaria. However, many <u>consumers</u> in poor countries can't afford them. Aid groups say it is necessary to change the <u>structure</u> of the way mosquito nets are distributed—they should be given away for free.

Write the letter of the correct definition next to each word.

Example: __*d*__ predominant

_____ **1.** structure

_____ **2.** consumers

_____ **3.** expose

_____ **4.** regions

_____ **5.** eliminate

a. get rid of something completely

b. those who buy or use goods and services

c. fairly large areas of a state, country, etc., usually without exact limits

d. more powerful, common, or noticeable than others

e. put someone in a situation or place that could be harmful or dangerous

f. the way in which relationships between people or groups are organized in a society

Use the academic words from the exercise above to complete the sentences.

6. It is important not to _____ children to lead paint.

7. The _____ of a beehive is amazing.

8. Scientists work to _____ disease.

Complete the sentences with your own ideas.

Example: The predominant language in the United States is _____*English*_____.

9. The region I live in is _____.

10. Consumers must shop carefully to find _____.

REMEMBER A root is the base part of a word. Many English roots come from Greek and Latin, such as the roots *micro, scope, bio, vis, epi,* and *dem.* Knowing just a few roots can help you define many words.

Look at the chart below. Define each word, based on the meaning of its root.

Root	Meaning	Word	Meaning
micro	small	microscope	*An optical instrument that magnifies objects too small to be seen by the naked eye*
1. scope	to see	telescope	
2. bio	life	biology	
3. vis	to see	invisible	
4. epi	upon, over, or attached to	epicenter	
5. dem	people	democracy	

Underline the root in each word. Then write the definition of the root and the word. Use a dictionary as necessary.

Example: microbe ___*small   a small organism*___

6. bionic _____

7. micron _____

8. periscope _____

9. demography _____

10. visualize _____

READING STRATEGY | **ANALYZE DIFFERENT KINDS OF TEXTS**

Use with textbook page 433.

> **REMEMBER** Learning to analyze different kinds of texts can help you to figure out if the sources you use when you research a topic are appropriate. Sources can vary widely in terms of content, reliability, and focus.

Read each paragraph below. Then answer the questions.

There are many reasons why the influenza epidemic of 1918–1919 was so deadly. People from many different countries were thrown together during World War I. The disease spread quickly around the world as soldiers returned home. Many cities created laws to try to slow down the disease. These laws included ordering people to wear masks and making spitting illegal. But the virus still killed between 20 and 50 million people.

1. In which class would you most likely read a text like the one above?

_____

2. What details in the text above helped you to answer question number 1?

_____

In 2005, scientists reconstructed the virus that killed so many people during the influenza epidemic of 1918–1919. Using small pieces of lung tissues saved from three victims who died of the disease, scientists made some important discoveries. They learned that this virus was a bird flu that jumped directly to people. They also found it had certain genetic mutations that made it especially deadly.

3. In which class would you most likely read a text like the one above?

_____

4. What is one important aspect of the influenza you can learn from the second text that you can't from the first?

_____

5. How do you think the strategy of analyzing different kinds of texts can help you to become a better researcher?

_____

_____

Choose the best answer for each item. Circle the letter of the correct answer.

1. A round red rash, swollen glands, and purple or black spots on the skin are signs

   of _____.

   a. a rat bite   **b.** the plague   **c.** typhus

2. The plague is caused by _____.

   a. ticks   **b.** a virus   **c.** bacteria

3. The plague reached almost every country in Europe because _____.

   a. of infected rats   **b.** people with the   **c.** dead people were
       and fleas   plague traveled   thrown onto the roads

4. In the 1300s, doctors tried to protect themselves against plague with _____.

   a. vaccines   **b.** special costumes   **c.** a microscope

5. The chances of a plague epidemic today are slight because scientists now

   know _____.

   a. where the infected   **b.** why the plague died out   **c.** what causes the plague
       rats live   in Europe and Asia   and how it spreads

EXTENSION   *Use with textbook page 441.*

Outbreak makes the point that as terrible as the plague was, some good things happened as a result of it. Think about something bad that has happened to you. Then write about how that event has made you a better person.

_____

_____

_____

_____

_____

GRAMMAR

Verb Tense in Reported Speech *Use with textbook page 442.*

> **REMEMBER** In reported speech there is a reporting verb, such as *said, asked,* or *told,* in the main clause. The main clause is followed by a noun clause. If the reporting verb is in the past, the verb in the noun clause often changes to the past.
> **Example:** Ling said, "It is critical to understand this issue." →
>   Ling said that it was critical to understand this issue.
> If the statement in the quoted speech is a general truth, the verb in the noun clause often remains in the present, even when the reporting verb is in the past.
> **Example:** The teacher stated, "Jupiter is the largest planet in the solar system." →
>   The teacher stated that Jupiter is the largest planet in the solar system.

Change the quoted speech below to reported speech.

Example: The woman said, "I have a large vegetable garden."

The woman said that she had a large vegetable garden.

1. The article said, "Many vegetables and fruits that we eat are native to North or South America."

   _____

2. The author stated, "Europeans discovered tomatoes, maize (corn), potatoes, and sweet potatoes when they came to America."

   _____

3. The author explained, "Potatoes and tomatoes belong to the same family."

   _____

4. The author mentioned, "Many people believed that tomatoes were poisonous."

   _____

5. My mother said, "Sweet potatoes are one of my favorite foods."

   _____

Include Quotations and Citations *Use with textbook page 443.*

This is the word web that Chelsea completed before writing her paragraph.

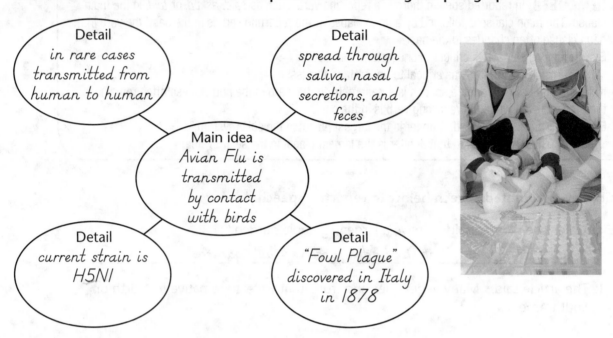

Detail
*in rare cases
transmitted from
human to human*

Detail
*spread through
saliva, nasal
secretions, and
feces*

Main idea
*Avian Flu is
transmitted
by contact
with birds*

Detail
*current strain is
H5N1*

Detail
*"Fowl Plague"
discovered in Italy
in 1878*

Complete your own word web based on your research about a disease. Include your main idea and supporting details.

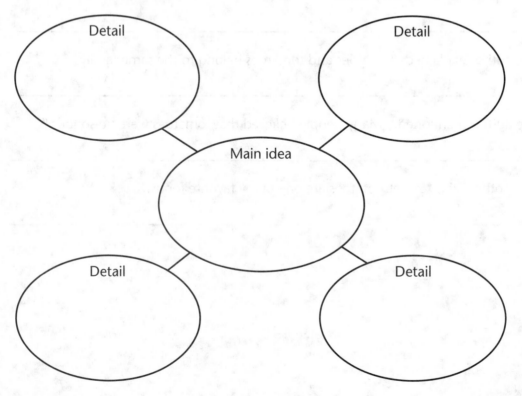

Detail

Detail

Main idea

Detail

Detail

Do things really change?

READING 3: From *Dateline: Troy*

VOCABULARY **Literary Words** *Use with textbook page 445.*

> **REMEMBER** The **theme** of a literary work is the main message or idea that it expresses. **Tone** is the feeling or attitude that a literary work expresses.

Label the descriptions as theme or tone.

Theme or tone?	Description
theme	having friends is important
1.	don't spend money you don't have
2.	suspenseful
3.	cheerful

Read the following passage and then circle the letter of the word or words that best complete each sentence.

> I can't believe tomorrow is the first day of school. I'll be a senior this year! It seems like just yesterday that I was a freshman. I remember how scared I was on my first day. The school seemed so big. Sure enough, I got lost trying to get to my first class. I stood in the hallway and panicked. But this nice senior asked me if I needed help finding my classroom. Relieved, I said, "Yes." She walked me right to my classroom door. Tomorrow, if I see a freshman who looks lost, I will be sure to stop and help her.

4. The tone of the passage is _____.

   a. reflective   **b.** angry   **c.** gloomy

5. The theme of the passage is _____.

   a. it's important to   **b.** high school lasts   **c.** small acts of kindness
   tell the truth   four years   can have a big effect

Read the paragraph below. Pay attention to the underlined academic words.

Though he knew stealing was not <u>ethical</u>, Tom the diamond thief was greedy. He decided to steal the valuable Blue Diamond from the museum. As he <u>approached</u> the diamond, he thought about how rich he would be. He was so sure of his abilities to escape quickly, he <u>ignored</u> the alarm set on the diamond's case. He didn't have a <u>notion</u> that he could be caught. When the alarm went off, the museum doors locked. All Tom could do was to hide in a corner of the room, <u>rigid</u> with fear. The police easily found and arrested Tom. He went to jail for the crime he had <u>committed</u>.

Write academic words from the paragraph above next to their correct definitions.

Example: _approached_ : moved closer

1. _____: morally good and correct

2. _____: stiff and not moving or bending

3. _____: an idea, belief, or opinion about something, especially one that you think is wrong

4. _____: didn't pay any attention

5. _____: did something wrong or illegal

Use academic words from the paragraph above to complete the sentences.

6. Do you think it is _____ to accept the money?

7. I don't agree with the _____ that you can't improve.

8. My dog's tail becomes _____ when she sees a stranger.

Complete the sentences with your own ideas.

Example: Some people don't think it is ethical to _test products on animals_ .

9. I ignored the rules when I _____.

10. As I approached school, I realized _____.

WORD STUDY   Homographs *Use with textbook page 447.*

> **REMEMBER** A homograph is a word that is spelled the same as another word but has a different meaning, part of speech, or pronunciation. For example, as a noun, *buffet* means "a table of food." As a verb, *buffet* means "to toss around." Use context clues to figure out if the homograph is a noun or verb. Knowing the part of speech helps you figure out the meaning.

Write the definition for each pair of homographs in the chart.

Homograph	Part of Speech	Meaning
present	noun	*gift*
present	verb	*to give something in a formal manner*
1. produce	noun	
2. produce	verb	
3. refuse	noun	
4. refuse	verb	

Write the definition of each homograph. Then write the part of speech.

Examples: The <u>wind</u> blew all night. _*moving air, noun*_____

Wind the yarn tightly. _*to twist, verb*_____

5. She <u>dove</u> into the pool. _____

6. A <u>dove</u> is a bird. _____

7. The <u>contract</u> will be signed soon. _____

8. Many people will <u>contract</u> the disease. _____

9. The Gobi <u>desert</u> is in Asia. _____

10. It is a crime to <u>desert</u> the military. _____

Use with textbook page 447.

> **REMEMBER** When you read, make generalizations about the text. A generalization is a statement or rule that applies to most examples and can be supported by facts.
> **Example:** Many ancient cities were surrounded by walls.

Read the passages and answer the questions.

My school is just like most schools. It has classes, lunch, gym, and after-school sports. Many different kinds of students go there. Some are athletes, others are artists, and others are kids who love science. Like students everywhere, many students in my school don't always make it to class on time. Mrs. Gray patrols the corridors, looking for students who are late.

1. What generalization does the author make about his school in the passage above?

_____

_____

2. Which details in the passage above are provided to support the generalization?

_____

_____

My hometown is like a lot of American towns. It has a main street with a post office and a drugstore where you can buy candy and magazines. But most American towns don't have a famous inventor like Ethan Hall living there. Most towns just have regular people. Ethan Hall has made my hometown a special place.

3. What generalizations does the author make about his hometown in the passage above?

_____

_____

4. Which statement in the passage above is not a generalization?

_____

5. What generalization can you make about the writer of the passage above?

_____

_____

COMPREHENSION *Use with textbook page 454.*

Choose the best answer for each item. Circle the letter of the correct answer.

1. Odysseus decided to trick the Trojans with a _____.

   a. unicorn   **b.** large real horse   **c.** large wooden horse

2. Two people who warned the Trojans not to bring the horse into their city
   were _____.

   a. Sinon and Odysseus   **b.** Hecuba and Priam   **c.** Laocoön and Cassandra

3. As a result, the person killed by serpents was _____.

   a. Odysseus   **b.** Hecuba   **c.** Laocoön

4. The Trojans brought the horse into Troy because they thought it was an offering
   to _____.

   a. Athena   **b.** Zeus   **c.** Achilles

5. After the Greeks destroyed Troy, they _____.

   a. lived happy ever after   **b.** ruled the world   **c.** suffered greatly

RESPONSE TO LITERATURE *Use with textbook page 455.*

**What do you think might have happened if the Trojans had not brought the horse
into their city? Imagine an alternative ending to the story and write it on the
lines below.**

_____

_____

_____

_____

_____

Passive Voice: Overview of Verb Forms

Use with textbook page 456.

> **REMEMBER** Sentences in the passive voice focus on the receiver of the action. All forms of the passive voice contain a form of the verb *be* + the past participle.
> **Examples:** Our Spanish class is taught by a teacher from Mexico.
> The telephone was invented by Alexander Graham Bell.
> The surveys have just been completed.
> By 1350, a third of Europe's population had been killed by plague.
> A cure for cancer will eventually be found.
> Note that the *by*-phrase may be omitted if the performer of the action is unknown or is not as important as the receiver of the action.

Rewrite the active-voice sentences below in the passive voice. Decide whether or not the *by*-phrase should be used.

Example: The general has given the orders.

The orders have been given by the general.

1. They have fought the most important battle of the war.

   _____

2. Cassandra predicted the outcome of the Trojan War.

   _____

3. Archeologists had discovered the site of Troy by the end of the nineteenth century.

   _____

4. They will sign the peace treaty in a special ceremony tomorrow.

   _____

5. Poets and historians still tell the story of the Trojan War and its aftermath.

   _____

WRITING

Include Paraphrases and Citations *Use with textbook page 457.*

This is the graphic organizer that Jack completed before writing his paragraph.

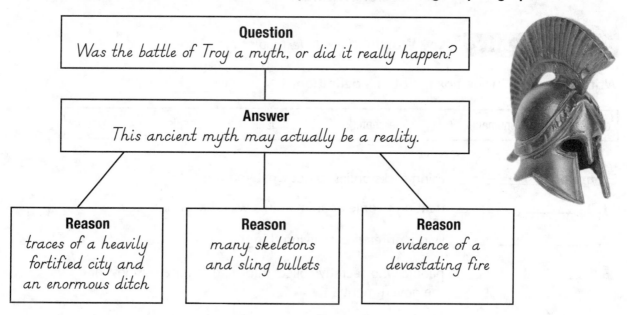

Question
Was the battle of Troy a myth, or did it really happen?

Answer
This ancient myth may actually be a reality.

Reason
traces of a heavily fortified city and an enormous ditch

Reason
many skeletons and sling bullets

Reason
evidence of a devastating fire

Complete your own graphic organizer about a person or place that people aren't sure existed. Include reasons that support your answer.

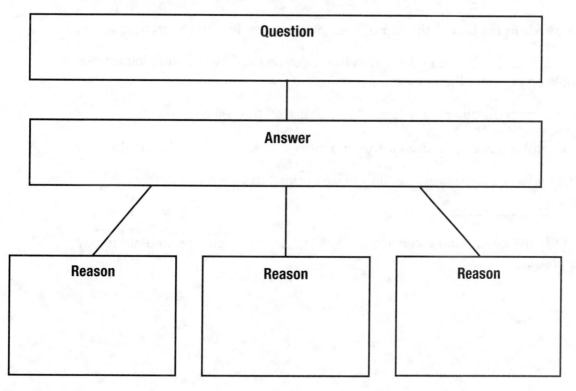

Question

Answer

Reason

Reason

Reason

Do things really change?

READING 4: From *Top Secret: A Handbook of Codes, Ciphers, and Secret Writing*

VOCABULARY **Key Words** *Use with textbook page 459.*

Write each word in the box next to its definition.

devious	humane	intercepted	organic	spies	tactic

Example: ____*devious*____: using tricks or lies to get what you want

1. _____: treating people or animals in a way that is kind

2. _____: living, or relating to living things

3. _____: people who secretly collect information for a business or the government

4. _____: a skillfully planned action to achieve something

5. _____: stopped something that is going from one place to another

Use the words in the box at the top of the page to complete the sentences.

6. _____ lead dangerous lives because they try to gather information people do not want them to have.

7. A player from the other team _____ the ball.

8. A compost is made up of dead leaves and other _____ matter.

9. What we were doing wasn't working so we decided to switch to a different

_____.

10. I felt like the salesperson was being _____ so I decided not to buy the product.

VOCABULARY **Academic Words** *Use with textbook page 460.*

Read the paragraph below. Pay attention to the underlined academic words.

Secret messages have been used for many <u>strategic</u> purposes over the years. In times of war, they have often been used to communicate <u>intelligence</u> about the enemy. One easy way to create secret messages is to write them in invisible ink. Invisible ink can be <u>traced</u> back to the times of the Greeks and Romans. One doesn't need expensive <u>equipment</u> to create invisible ink. Following a few simple <u>instructions</u>, you can make invisible ink from everyday household items. You might even want to create a <u>code</u> that only your friend can understand.

Write the letter of the correct definition next to each word.

Example: ___*d*___ equipment

_____ 1. intelligence

_____ 2. traced

_____ 3. strategic

_____ 4. instructions

_____ 5. code

a. a system of words, letters, or signs that are used instead of ordinary writing to keep something secret

b. studied or described the history, development, or origin of something

c. information or advice that tells you how to do something

d. the tools or machines that you need for a particular activity

e. information about the secret activities of others

f. having a military, business, or political purpose

Use the academic words from the exercise above to complete the sentences.

6. The company made a _____ business decision to move its offices.

7. During a war, each side tries to gather _____ about the other side.

8. The detective wrote his notes in _____.

Complete the sentences with your own ideas.

Example: One piece of equipment you need for camping is a _____*tent*_____.

9. My ancestors can be traced back to _____.

10. I had to read instructions to learn how to _____.

REMEMBER The letter *c* can stand for the soft sound /s/ as in *excel* and the hard sound /k/ as in *corn*. The letter *g* can stand for the soft sound /j/ as in *gentle* or the hard sound /g/ as in *goat*. The letters *c* and *g* have soft sounds when followed by *e*, *i*, or *y*.

Read the words in the box below. Then write each word in the correct column in the chart. You will have words left over.

~~center~~	contagious	angel	celebrate	challenge
gum	icicle	generous	gate	Egypt
guess	policy	wagon	lucid	grape
egg	crack	clobber	soccer	concrete

Soft *c*	Soft *g*
center	

Write the letter-sound pattern in each word below.

Example: gem   *soft g*

1. voice   _____

2. recess   _____

3. wage   _____

4. giraffe   _____

5. twice   _____

6. gelatin   _____

READING STRATEGY | **IDENTIFY MAIN IDEAS**   *Use with textbook page 461.*

> **REMEMBER** When you read an informational text, identify the main, or most important, idea in each paragraph and section. Use the headings and key words to help you identify main ideas.

Follow the directions for each passage and answer the questions.

Nutritional Value of Vegetables

Potatoes taste good boiled, mashed, and roasted. They're also good for you. Potatoes contain many vitamins, such as Vitamins B1, B2, B3, and Vitamin C. They also contain minerals such as iron and calcium. Potatoes aren't very high in calories, either. That is, unless you load them up with lots of butter and sour cream!

---

1. Look at the heading of the passage above and skim the passage for key words. What do you think the main idea is?

   _____

2. Now read the passage. Think about the main idea. Write a summary.

   _____

   _____

A Pet Owner's Responsibilities

There is more to owning a cat than playing with it. Being a pet owner is a big responsibility. Cats need clean water and fresh cat food every day. They need to go to the veterinarian every year. It's a lot of work to take care of a cat.

---

3. Look at the heading of the passage above and skim the passage for key words. What do you think the main idea is?

   _____

4. Now read the passage. Think about the main idea. Write a summary.

   _____

   _____

5. How can identifying the main idea help you to read with greater comprehension?

   _____

   _____

Choose the best answer for each item. Circle the letter of the correct answer.

1. Two ways of concealing a message in ancient times were to _____.

   a. sew it into embroidery and use text messages on a cell phone
   b. buy lots of cigars and send coded messages by telegraph
   c. tattoo it on the skull and sew a message into the sole of a sandal

2. A concealed message saved the life of _____.

   a. a World War II spy
   b. Sir John Trevanion
   c. Helen of Troy

3. Invisible inks are either organic or _____.

   a. chemical
   b. mineral
   c. electronic

4. To develop organic invisible inks such as juice or vinegar, you need to put _____.

   a. a pencil point on the message
   b. ashes on the message
   c. direct heat on the message

5. One of the drawbacks of invisible ink is that you cannot use it _____.

   a. to send a lot of information
   b. to write on the other side of a real letter
   c. to write on fibrous paper

EXTENSION *Use with textbook page 469.*

Write a secret message using code. Be sure to include a key to the code the reader must use to read the secret message!

_____

_____

_____

_____

_____

_____

GRAMMAR

Adverb Clauses of Time: *since (then), when, once, after*

Use with textbook page 470.

> **REMEMBER** An adverb clause of time tells when something happened. It describes the relationship between two events. *Since* + a main clause tells about something that began at a specific time in the past and continues into the present. To avoid repetition, the expression *since then* can be used to refer back to a specific time in the past that has been mentioned before.
> **Examples:** Since the tomatoes ripened, we have eaten tomatoes every night.
> The tomatoes ripened in August. Since then, we have eaten tomatoes every night.
> *When, once,* and *after* + a main clause show that one event happens and another event happens soon after it. The adverb clause of time expresses the first event; the main clause expresses the second event.
> **Examples:** When it is hot and sunny, tomatoes ripen quickly.

Join each pair of sentences with the adverb in parentheses. Be sure to place the adverb before the clause that describes what happened first. (You may need to rearrange the order of the clauses.)

Example: (after) I celebrated. I passed the test.

  After I passed the test, I celebrated.

1. (when) It began to rain. We opened our umbrellas.

   _____

2. (once) They explained the rules. We understood how to play the game.

   _____

3. (after) They had worked hard. They were ready for a rest.

   _____

4. (when) Everyone started to dance. The music began.

   _____

5. (once) No one wanted to swim in the ocean. It got cold.

   _____

Support Ideas with Examples *Use with textbook page 471.*

This is the main-idea web that Will completed before writing his paragraph.

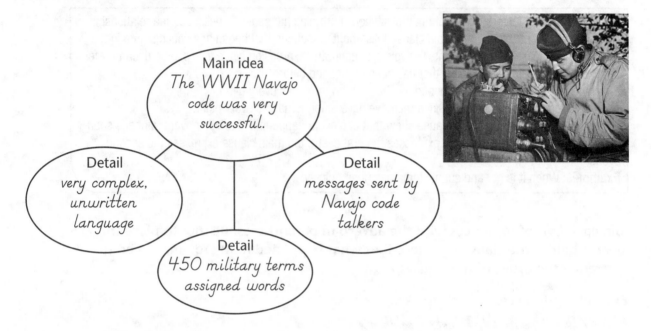

Main idea
The WWII Navajo code was very successful.

Detail
very complex, unwritten language

Detail
messages sent by Navajo code talkers

Detail
450 military terms assigned words

Complete your own main-idea web for a research report about a concealment technique used in the past or present. List your main idea and details.

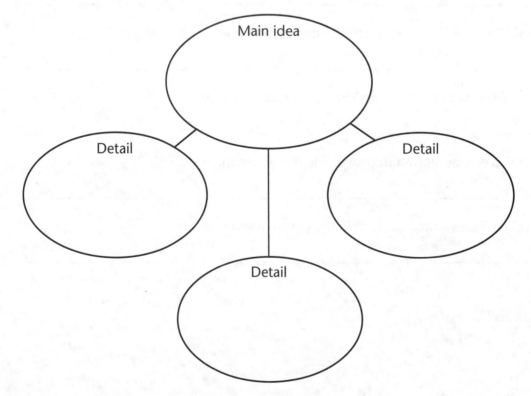

Main idea

Detail

Detail

Detail

Do things really change?

UNIT 6

READING 5: "Solving the Mystery of Marfa's Lights" / "Marfa's Legendary Lights"

TEXT ANALYSIS   Informational Texts   *Use with textbook page 473.*

> **REMEMBER** **Informational texts** provide factual details about a topic. They often answer the questions *who, what, when, where,* and *why.* You will find informational texts in magazines, nonfiction books, the Internet, and newspapers. When you read an informational text, you should skim and then scan the article. Notice the title, subheadings, boldface words, and any pictures. Before you start reading, try to figure out what the text is about.

1. Skim the informational text below. Based on the title, what do you think the article is about?

   _____

   _____

2. Scan the text below. Based on reading the boldface words and the first sentence, what else can you learn before you read?

   _____

   _____

3. Read the paragraph. What is the main idea and major supporting details?

   _____

   _____

Types of Climate in the United States

   The United States is a large country with many different types of climates. The northern region, including Alaska, has a **polar** climate. Hawaii and southern Florida have a **tropical** climate. The northwest coast of Washington and Oregon has a **marine** climate, and the climate along the California coast is **Mediterranean**. The United States also has mountainous regions such as the Rockies, which have an **alpine** climate. Parts of Nevada, California, Utah, and Arizona have a **desert** climate. Most of the southern United States is **humid subtropical** and most of the northern United States is **humid continental**, with cold winters and warm summers.

> **REMEMBER** A good **procedural text** should clearly explain how to do something from start to finish. It should break the process into simple steps and be easy for the reader to understand. It should also anticipate readers' questions and needs.

Read and evaluate the procedural text below. Then answer the questions below.

How to Wash a Dog

First, you'll need some type of plastic basin or tub. You may prefer to wash your dog outdoors, particularly if he or she is very dirty. Try to keep your dog warm at all times. It's a good idea to comb the dog's hair before you get him or her wet. Make sure the water is warm (not too hot) before you put the dog in the tub. Once the dog is in the tub and wet, apply small amounts of soap. Begin at the neck and work your way toward the tail. Also, if you have one, you should put down a rubber mat so the dog doesn't slide in the tub (this can make dogs nervous). It's also a good idea to put cotton balls in the dog's ears, so water doesn't get in. Then rinse the dog. Be sure to get the soap out. Then towel dry. You can even use a blow dryer!

---

1. Do you think these instructions would enable you to wash your dog successfully? Why or why not?

   _____

   _____

2. Where might a reader become confused or need additional information?

   _____

   _____

3. Which parts could be clearer, more detailed, or better organized?

   _____

   _____

TEXT ANALYSIS **Using Graphic Sources** *Use with textbook page 476.*

> **REMEMBER** Graphic sources, such as charts and graphs, provide information visually. To understand a graphic source, you need to examine the title and the labels. When you analyze multiple graphic sources, you need to determine what the sources have in common and how they differ.

The charts below show the recreational activities available in Wildlife Management Areas (WMA) in two regions. Read the information in the charts and then answer the questions below.

Wildlife Management Areas in the Hill Country Region

Name of WMA	Biking	Camping	Hiking	Hunting	Fishing
Granger	√	√	√	√	√
Kerr	√			√	√
Mason Mountain				√	
Old Tunnel			√		
Walter Buck	√		√	√	

Wildlife Management Areas in the Panhandle Plains Region

Name of WMA	Biking	Camping	Hiking	Hunting	Fishing
Gene Howe	√	√	√	√	√
Matador		√	√	√	√
Playa Lakes, Taylor Lakes Unit			√	√	
Playa Lakes, Dimmitt Unit				√	

1. Which region allows the greater number of recreational activities, Hill Country or

   Panhandle Plains? _____

2. Which region allows more biking, Hill Country or Panhandle Plains? _____

3. How many of the Wildlife Management Areas allow camping? _____

4. Which Wildlife Management Area allows the most recreational activities?

   _____

REMEMBER Informational and procedural writing often contain graphics, or visual aids, such as charts, maps, and diagrams. They provide useful information in picture form. They often have labels, titles, and captions that provide extra information and help you understand.

Read and evaluate the chart below. How clear is the information in it? Answer the questions below.

Participation in Various Leisure Activities

Activity	Male	Female
Movies	59.5	60.5
Playing sports	38.8	22.7
Sports events	41.4	29.2
Home repair	46.3	38.9
Charity work	25.6	32.1
Gardening	37.1	56.7
Amusement park	40.4	42.9

Data from U.S. National Endowment for the Arts

1. Does the graphic look good? _____

_____

2. Is a graphic the best way to provide facts in this case? Why or why not?

_____

_____

3. Is the information in the graphic clear? _____

_____

4. If not, what could be done to make the graphic clearer? What information would you

   add? _____

_____

_____

TEXT ANALYSIS **Same Topic, Different Viewpoint**
Use with textbook page 477.

> **REMEMBER** In informational writing, an author's **point of view** is his or her attitude toward the topic. An author's point of view influences the way that the author presents information. Different authors may have very different points of view on the same topic.

Reread Bryn Bayard's "Outbreak: Plagues that Changed History." Pay attention to the author's purpose and supporting details. Then compare it with the excerpt below and answer the questions that follow.

From Daniel Defoe's
History of the Plague in London (1722)

> Till this week the city continued free, there having never any died except that one Frenchman, who I mentioned before, within the whole ninety-seven parishes. Now, there died four within the city, one in Wood Street, one in Fenchurch Street, and two in Crooked Lane. Southwark was entirely free, having not one yet died on that side of the water.
>
> . . . This was a very terrible and melancholy thing to see, and as it was a sight which I could not but look on from morning to night (for indeed there was nothing else of moment to be seen), it filled me with very serious thoughts of the misery that was coming upon the city, and the unhappy condition of those that would be left in it.

1. What do Bayard's and Defoe's articles have in common?

   _____

   _____

2. Do the two articles seem to have the same purpose? If not, how are they different? Provide support from the texts in your answer.

   _____

   _____

   _____

Summarizing and Critiquing Text
Use with textbook page 478.

> **REMEMBER** When you **summarize** a text, you tell the main idea and the most important details of the text, without adding your opinion. When you **critique** a text, you evaluate the information the author presents and how he or she presents it.

Read the following two paragraphs. Then answer the questions below.

> **A.** Beverly Gherman's biography *Jimmy Carter* tells the story of the former president's life. She describes Jimmy Carter's rural childhood in Georgia, his military service, and his experiences before, during, and after his presidency. In addition, Gherman discusses what many people regard as Carter's successes and failures as president.
>
> **B.** Beverly Gherman's biography *Jimmy Carter* provides an interesting and insightful glimpse into the former U.S. president's life. One of the biography's greatest strengths is the way Gherman describes important events in Carter's life, some of which influenced his political ideas. For example, she describes his experiences dealing with racial segregation in the South before the Civil Rights Movement.

1. Which paragraph is a summary? Which is a critique? Explain your answer.

   _____

   _____

   _____

2. Choose a book or story you remember well. On the lines below, write two short paragraphs. The first paragraph should be a summary, and the second paragraph should be a critique.

   _____

   _____

   _____

   _____

   _____

   _____

   _____

WRITING   **Finding Sources** *Use with textbook page 485.*

This is the chart that Rita used for her topic.

What I Already Know	What I Need to Know	Where I Might Find This Information
• aurora borealis or "Northern Lights" appear at night in northern regions	• What is the cause of the Northern Lights? • How often do they occur?	• a scientific website • a scientific reference book

Complete your own chart before you begin your research report. Discuss your ideas with a partner.

What I Already Know	What I Need to Know	Where I Might Find This Information

This is the chart that Rita created after evaluating many sources and deciding which was the most reliable. She quoted the information, paraphrased it, and listed the source in MLA format.

Information	Paraphrase	Source
"Researchers have discovered that explosions of magnetic energy a third of the way to the moon power substorms that cause the Northern Lights."	"Magnetic storms cause the Northern Lights."	Brown, Dwayne and Layton, Laura. "NASA Satellites Discover What Powers Northern Lights". 24 July 2008. www.nasa.gov

Complete your own chart as you prepare your research report.

Information	Paraphrase	Source

EDIT AND PROOFREAD *Use with textbook page 496.*

Read the paragraph below carefully. Look for mistakes in spelling, punctuation, and grammar. Correct the mistakes with the editing marks on Student Book page 563. Then rewrite the paragraph correctly on the lines below.

Each year the Teachers at Liberty High School challenge the student basketball team to a game And for the last for years, the teachers, despite their advanced age and poor physical condition, has won. Thats because the teachers have a secret weapon: Mr Foley. he is 6 feet, 7 inches tall This year's game started the way all the Others started. Mr. Foley win the tip-off for the teachers. But this year the students realize they can outrun the teachers. The students score several baskets. But every time they missed, Mr. Foley got the rebound. With five seconds left in the game, the teachers has a one-point led. It look like this game would end like all the others. But wait, the students have the ball! One of them desperately shoots the ball at the basket from mid-court. The ball goes in! the Students win!

_____

_____

_____

_____

_____

_____

_____

_____

Underline the vocabulary items you know and can use well. Review and practice any you haven't underlined. Underline them when you know them well.

Literary Words	Key Words	Academic Words	
first-person point of view	epidemic	consented	approached
third-person point of view	fragility	economics	committed
theme	host	reaction	ethical
tone	immune	status	ignored
	society	tradition	notion
	stages	consumers	rigid
	devious	eliminate	code
	humane	expose	equipment
	intercepted	predominant	instructions
	organic	regions	intelligence
	spies	structure	strategic
	tactic		traced

Put a check by the skills you can perform well. Review and practice any you haven't checked off. Check them off when you can perform them well.

Skills	I can . . .
Word Study	☐ recognize and spell words with silent letters. ☐ recognize and use word roots. ☐ recognize and use homographs. ☐ recognize and spell words with soft *c* and soft *g*.
Reading Strategies	☐ ask questions (5Ws). ☐ analyze different kinds of texts. ☐ make generalizations. ☐ identify main ideas.
Grammar	☐ use relative pronouns as subjects and objects. ☐ use the correct verb forms in reported speech. ☐ use passive voice correctly. ☐ use adverb clauses of time: *since (then)*, *when*, *once*, *after*.
Writing	☐ write an introductory paragraph. ☐ include quotations and citations. ☐ include paraphrases and citations. ☐ support ideas with examples. ☐ write a research report.

Visual Literacy: Smithsonian American
Art Museum *Use with textbook pages 498–499.*

LEARNING TO LOOK

Look at *Feast Bracelet* by Richard Mawdsley on page 498 in your textbook.
Describe six things that you see. State facts, not opinions.

Example: _____*The pie is missing a piece!*_____

1. _____   4. _____

2. _____   5. _____

3. _____   6. _____

INTERPRETATION

Look at *Feast Bracelet* again. If you could create an invitation for this feast, what
would you do? Think about how you want your guests to dress (formally or
informally), what time they should come, the type of event you're having (birthday
party, dinner, etc.), where the event will take place, and any other event details
you can think of. Write your own invitation below.

Invitation

Example: _____*You are invited to my birthday party on . . . . .*_____

_____

_____

_____

_____

_____

_____

_____

Look at *Ghost Clock* by Wendell Castle on page 499 in your textbook. If you could interview the artist about this work of art, what would you ask him? Use *Who, Where, When, What, Why,* and *How* to shape your questions.

Example: Why ___*is this called Ghost Clock?*___

7. Who _____

_____

8. Where _____

_____

9. When _____

_____

10. What _____

_____

11. Why _____

_____

12. How _____

_____

MEDIA LITERACY

Now that you have read about change and how something old can become new, go to www.LongmanKeystone.com for links to the Smithsonian website. Follow the online instructions to compare the artwork in your student book with other media that convey similar messages. Which messages are conveyed more directly through visual media? Which ideas are conveyed more effectively through print or audio?

TEST PREPARATION

UNIT 1 TEST 1

DIRECTIONS
Read the selection. Then answer the questions that follow it.

Help Others, Help Yourself

Volunteerism is a cornerstone of every society. The desire to help others in their everyday struggles, whether financial, emotional, or physical, creates a foundation for community that cannot be created through any other personal interaction. The volunteer cements the society in which he or she serves by giving the society a sense of compassion for people in need.

Volunteering also has benefits for those who offer their time and effort to others. A volunteer receives as much as or more than he or she gives. Volunteerism keeps the mind sharp, especially in older adults. It decreases the loss of cognitive and memory function by eliminating social isolation. People who volunteer form connections with other volunteers, the people they serve, and the community in which they live. The joy of volunteering has been shown to decrease stress, a significant factor in many heart-related illnesses. Sometimes volunteer work can lead to a permanent job. But perhaps most importantly, volunteering increases one's sense of purpose, without which many people struggle from day to day. As Frederick Nietzsche once said, "He who has a why to live can bear almost any how."

---

1   How does volunteering help society in general?

   A   By reducing the stress levels of volunteers

   B   By decreasing the social isolation of volunteers

   C   By creating opportunities for permanent jobs

   D   By giving society a sense of compassion for those in need

2   What is the meaning of the quote at the end of the passage?

   F   People who have a sense of purpose can better cope with difficulty.

   G   For volunteers to be effective, they must be well-trained.

   H   Volunteers have a special wisdom about life and living.

   J   People who help others often question why others suffer.

UNIT 1 TEST 2

DIRECTIONS
Read the selection. Then answer the questions that follow it.

The Test

Martin was sitting on the city bus, daydreaming and trying to get his stressful day out of his head. He watched the Boston brownstones pass by as the bus moved from street to street. He imagined if the people inside the homes were having the day he was. Martin had been looking for a job without success for a long time now. He was down to his last five-dollar bill. He was angry with himself for spending money on the bus ride, which was now a luxury, but he was simply too tired to walk.

Martin left the bus and began to walk the block towards his home. He popped into a local store to get some bread. He still had some peanut butter left at home, and that would last him a while if he was careful. He stood in line while a woman holding a screaming infant stood in front of him. She was frantically arguing with the clerk. "I can pay tomorrow. He has a fever and I need this medicine. I can't afford a doctor. Please." The clerk was very upset, but he was a young man and kept explaining that it might cost him his job to do that.

Martin didn't hesitate. He put his bread back on a nearby shelf and handed the woman the five-dollar bill from his pocket. She looked at him, stunned, then teared up as she took the money. "Thank you so much," she said. Martin just nodded. The woman paid, took the medicine, and left quickly.

Martin sighed and began to leave the store when a man tapped his shoulder. "I can tell you needed that money," the man said.

"The baby needed it more," Martin said, sounding exhausted.

The man smiled and reached into his pocket. He pulled out a card and handed it to Martin. "I run a charity that helps the needy. I need someone to work with the people who come in. It's a good job and you're the perfect one for it."

Martin's eyes grew wide. "A job?" he asked.

"Yup," said the man. "It's yours. The address is on the card. See you tomorrow at 9 A.M."

The man paid for his soda and left. Martin stood in the doorway of the store and just stared out into the street.

---

1 What can you infer about Martin when he "didn't hesitate" to give the woman his money?

   A He knew he would get a job.

   B He is generous by nature.

   C He didn't really need the bread he was buying.

   D He was expecting a reward for his kindness.

2 What is the theme of the story?

   F There are needy people everywhere.

   G Some people are extremely lucky.

   H Generosity is always rewarded somehow.

   J Some people are afraid to help others.

UNIT 2 TEST 1

DIRECTIONS
Read the selection. Then answer the questions that follow it.

Telling

(1) Their is an old saying, "Do as I say and not as I do." (2) The statement really says that I want you to do the things that I don't. (3) It's very odd to make the statement because it tells others that you are sometimes hypocritical. (4) We show who we really are by our actions, not our words.

(5) How many times have we told others what is right and good and then done the opposite? (6) Humans make mistakes, we are imperfect beings. (7) However, if we want to believe we are good and trustworthy, we must BE good and trustworthy. (8) You cannot think yourself into a particular way of acting. (9) You have to act yourself into a particular way of thinking. (10) After all, as another famous saying goes "Actions speak louder than words."

---

1 What action would correct the error in sentence 1?

   A There are no errors.

   B Delete the quotation marks.

   C Change *Their* to *There*.

   D Change the colon to a comma.

2 What is the problem with sentence 6?

   F It should be two sentences.

   G It doesn't relate to the main idea.

   H It should be the final sentence of the passage.

   J It has spelling errors.

UNIT 2 TEST 2

DIRECTIONS
Read the selection. Then answer the questions that follow it.

The Long History of DNA

DNA has existed since life has existed. It is the means by which each generation passes its traits on to new generations. The discovery of DNA has led to marvelous scientific breakthroughs in the understanding and treatment of a variety of illnesses, from cancer to attention deficit disorder. The story of how we learned about DNA and what it does dates all the way back to 1868.

In 1868, a doctor in Switzerland named Frederich Meisher found something while studying cells. He isolated something he called *nuclein*, which was present in every cell he studied. What he found was part of our DNA strand. The "NA" of DNA stands for *nucleic acid*. Only two years later, a monk named Gregor Mendel completed his experiments with pea plants, which proved that plant traits could be manipulated and given to offspring in various ways. Separately, the two men had discovered the two most important aspects of how we pass our genes to our children: the existence of a cellular code and that genetics play a role in how traits are passed down from one generation to the next. It wouldn't be until 1953 that two American scientists presented a paper with the structure of the now famous double helix known as DNA. Both shared the Nobel Prize in 1963 with another scientist working in genetics. We have learned so much in fifty years thanks to the genius of many different scientists.

---

1 What did Federich Meisher contribute to the study of DNA?

    A He discovered that traits can be changed in each generation.

    B He found a new substance in every cell that was part of DNA.

    C He discovered the helix structure of DNA.

    D He learned how to transfer genetic traits between cells.

2 Based on the passage, it can be concluded that Gregor Mendel was performing what kind of experiments with pea plants?

    F He was pairing up plants with different traits to see what the next generation looked like.

    G He was dissecting the cells of plants and finding portions of the DNA helix.

    H He was watching pea plants grow in the wild and marveling at their diversity.

    J He was harvesting pea plants with different genetic traits and identifying their genes.

UNIT 3 TEST 1

DIRECTIONS
Read the selection. Then answer the questions that follow it.

Taking a Stand Against Bullies

District 201 schools will be holding a class for parents on bullying Thursday evening at 6:30 p.m. We will have three experts from various fields who will talk about bullying and what you can do as a parent to deal with this growing problem. The following will be addressed:

1. How to know if your child is being bullied

2. Ways to talk to your child about why bullying is wrong

3. Emotional versus physical bullying

4. What the school does when bullying is reported

5. Help for children who act out in anger

6. Counseling for both victims and those who bully

All are welcome to attend, whether your child has experienced bullying or not. It is important to deal with this serious issue. Our children deserve it.

---

1 What can be inferred from this passage?

   A District 201 has a terrible bullying problem.

   B Parents are completely ignorant of the issue.

   C The problem of bullying has become an important topic.

   D Little is known about why bullying occurs.

2 Which sentence best describes District 201 schools' approach to bullying.

   F They want to take a serious stand on bullying.

   G They want to reach out to both victims and bullies for help.

   H They want both parents and students to be involved.

   J They want to keep bullies out of schools.

UNIT 3 TEST 2

DIRECTIONS
Read the selection. Then answer the questions that follow it.

Simply Stand

(1) It does not matter, the strength of your legs.

(2) It does not matter, the strength of your shoulders.

(3) It does not matter, the strength of your hands.

(4) It does not matter, the strength of your sight.

(5) It does not matter, the strength of your voice.

(6) What matters the most is the strength of your choice.

(7) When you stand for something, you can never fall.

(8) Though the very powers of darkness and evil and hatred swoop upon you, you will never be beaten. Because, in the end, they who fight best simply stand.

---

1 Line 8 is an example of which literary device?

  A Metaphor

  B Simile

  C Characterization

  D Hyperbole

2 In the poem, which device does the author use to emphasize that strength lies in choice and not in the body?

  F Repetition

  G Hyperbole

  H Imagery

  J Personification

UNIT 4 TEST 1

DIRECTIONS
Read the selection. Then answer the questions that follow it.

Landing It

In her dojo, where she had been studying and practicing karate for four years, Trisha had avoided having to face another student in a match of skill. Sparring required a great deal of control because you had to make very slight contact without hitting your opponent. It was a very delicate sport. And Trisha had never done it.

Today, however, was a competition, and her sensei had encouraged her to compete for her dojo. She was the only girl in her age group. The judges debated whether to allow her to spar. Her sensei, however, talked to them, and they waved Trisha into the ring. She was terrified.

In the first round, Trisha's opponent landed a perfect, light hit to her side. It didn't hurt at all, except for her pride. He received a point. The second call of "*Hajime!*" and the two entered the ring again. This time Trisha landed a soft blow to her opponent's chest. Both warriors went to their corners and the flag came up over Trisha's head. Whoever won the next point would win the match.

The last round lasted a long time. Both Trisha and her opponent were blocking masterfully and nothing was landing. Then Trisha's opponent dropped both arms to block a low kick. With absolute grace and control she placed a roundhouse kick within an inch of her opponent's cheek without touching him. She had won her first sparring match.

---

1 Based on the context of the passage, which word means *master*?

   A Dojo

   B Sensei

   C Hajime

   D Spar

2 What obstacle did Trisha have to overcome during the match?

   F She had never sparred before.

   G Her opponent was bigger than she was.

   H She was not a good kicker.

   J The judges refused to let her compete.

UNIT 4 TEST 2

DIRECTIONS
Read the selection. Then answer the questions that follow it.

April 17, 1970

Apollo 13 launched on April 17, 1970. It was to be the third moon landing in U.S. history. However, it became one of the most harrowing space events in NASA history. It is classifieded by NASA as a "successful failure" because the crew made it back to Earth safely.

There was a comedy of errors before the flight even left Earth. One of the crew was exposed to German measles and was replaced a day before liftoff. Several engine parts required repair and replacement. The repair work on some parts of the craft damaged the oxygen tanks. No one knew this had happened. When *Apollo* lifted into space, all seemed to be going well. The crew even joked about their boredom.

A little over an hour into flight, there was an explosion. The number 2 oxygen tank had exploded. Precious air was leaking into space. The heating systems went down and temperatures dropped to near freezing. The craft had made a correction in the beginning of the flight plan and now could not use the navigation system to get back to Earth.

Ground control and Captain Lovell decided to use an alternative navigation system. However, that system had never been aligned. There are no markers in space to guide you. So ground control ran calculations, and the crew was able to use the sun to align the second navigation system. After seven grueling hours, *Apollo 13* landed safely to Earth with a very tired but happy crew.

---

1 What would be a good title for this passage?

   A A National Day of Mourning

   B Quick Thinking Prevents a Tragedy

   C An Unprepared Crew

   D How NASA Learned Its Lesson

2 How does the reader know that the crew was completely unaware that there would be trouble with the flight?

   F They complained of boredom.

   G They lifted off even with the damaged tanks.

   H The crew knew each other very well.

   J The heating system was working.

UNIT 5 TEST 1

DIRECTIONS
Read the selection. Then answer the questions that follow it.

The Bradshaw Conflict Management Team, L.L.C.

(1) Every office has conflicts. (2) It's part of the human condition. (3) In a typical company, Human Resources handles such conflicts. (4) However, constant conflict resolution can use up most of HR's time and result in other important projects being delayed. (5) That's where the Bradshaw Team comes in.

(6) The Bradshaw Team works only in conflict management. (7) We deal in everything, from coworkers who frustrate others with noisy work habits to extreme situations of harassment and crime. (8) Bradshaw's team of counselors, lawyers, and business experts will get your team working together like a well-oiled machine.

(9) ou may balk at hiring a service just for conflict, but you have to ask yourself this question: How much revenue are you losing to workers who can't be productive because they dislike their work environment and coworkers? (10) When you calculate the losses that come from worker conflict, you'll see that our services will pay for themselves.

(11) All consultations are free and confidential.

---

1 To what genre of writing does this passage belong?

   A Instruction

   B Biography

   C Advertising

   D Editorial

2 Which sentence from the passage is an opinion?

   F Sentence 3

   G Sentence 6

   H Sentence 8

   J Sentence 11

UNIT 5 TEST 2

DIRECTIONS
Read the selection. Then answer the questions that follow it.

March 5, Walton Knotch—The Township Board's troubles were still evident at last night's meeting in the community center of Walton Knotch. Supervisor Kent refused to call the meeting to order until Board Member Holliday apologized for his rant during the last meeting about Kent's lack of leadership. Because of this, the meeting began twenty minutes late, with Holliday refusing to apologize. Only outcries from the public to begin the meeting forced Kent to call everyone to order.

Even the Pledge of Allegiance became a fight, with each board member trying to speak over the other. A sacred oath to our country turned into a first-grade screaming match. When the board members were finally seated and the first order of business was read, Board Member Grady stood up and moved that the town charter be read. Her ally, Board Member Jones, seconded the motion. Kent joined them to break the tie and all 75 pages of the town charter were read aloud. This took three hours and cleared the hall of all but the press.

The town board has forgotten why it exists. It does not exist on its own, but because of and for the people. We hope the citizens of Walton Knotch remember this nonsense when the elections come up in April.

---

1   How were the conflicts in the town board affecting the public?

   A   No government business was getting done.

   B   People were enjoying the spectacle.

   C   Citizens stopped attending board meetings.

   D   People bought more newspapers to read about it.

2   What solution does the author suggest to the problem at the end of the passage?

   F   Boycotting town board meetings

   G   Having an expert meet with the board

   H   Having the public dissolve the town board

   J   Voting everybody out of office

UNIT 6 TEST 1

DIRECTIONS
Read the selection. Then answer the questions that follow it.

The Evolution of English

From *The Canterbury Tales: Prologue*

(The Canterbury Tales *was written in the thirteenth century by English poet Geoffrey Chaucer. It is a classic in world literature. Below, you will find two versions of the same selection from the poem. The first version is the original as it was written in Middle English. The second is a translation into modern English.*)

Whan zephirus eek with his sweete breeth
Inspired hath in every holt and heeth
Tendre croppes, and the yonge sonne
Hath in the ram his halve cours yronne…

When Zypher also with his sweet breath
Has breathed life into every valley and field's
Tender plants, and the young Sun
Has in the Ram half his course run…

---

1 Which of the following words remained unchanged as Middle English evolved into modern English?

A *With*

B *Half*

C *Also*

D *When*

2 Which of the following words means something completely different in modern English than it did in Middle English?

F *Tendre*

G *Eek*

H *Breeth*

J *Every*

UNIT 6 TEST 2

DIRECTIONS
Read the selection. Then answer the questions that follow it.

Section One

It's cold in here. Wait. Where am I? I don't remember falling asleep. I was just in bed. Bed. No, I got up this morning. Oh, wow, my head hurts. Who's that yelling? No, no, I'm fine. Wait. There's light coming in and out. I can't seem to open my eyes. Who's whistling? Yeah, I'm fine. Oh, the light is bright. Oh, wait. Grass. Coach. Helmet. Wow. I must have gotten hit really hard that time.

Section Two

Colleen is trying to get up, folks, but the medic won't let her until she's checked from head to foot for serious injuries. It looked like she wasn't responding for a few seconds there. Wait. She's nodding her head. She's all right, folks. She's answering questions and they're walking the stretcher back to the ambulance. Okay, folks, she's up and walking. Wow, listen to those cheers. It was a scary few minutes there, but it looks like Colleen is fine. Regent High's first female quarterback took quite a tackle and she walked away like a trooper.

---

1 Section one is written from whose perspective?

   A The coach's

   B The medic's

   C A teammate's

   D Colleen's

2 Who is the likely speaker in section two?

   F The coach

   G Colleen

   H An announcer

   J Colleen's parents